Building Research Establishment Report

Timber drying manual

G H Pratt, FIWSc

Princes Risborough Laboratory

Department of the Environment
Building Research Establishment

London, Her Majesty's Stationery Office
1974

Full details of all new BRE publications are published quarterly in BRE NEWS. Requests for BRE NEWS, or placing on the mailing list should be addressed to:

Distribution Unit
Application Services Division
Building Research Establishment
Garston Watford WD2 7JR

ISBN 0 11 670521 3

Preface

The Timber Drying Manual supersedes the Kiln Operators Handbook which was written by W. C. Stevens and G. H. Pratt and first published in 1952. Several new chapters have been added and the scope widened to make this Timber Drying Manual a complete guide to all methods of drying timber. With a total of more than sixty illustrations this book represents the culmination of nearly fifty years of research on timber drying at the Princes Risborough Laboratory.

In implementation of Government policy to transfer research done primarily in the interests of industry from national research establishments to industry itself, timber drying activities were transferred in 1974 from PRL to the Timber Research and Development Association, Hughenden Valley, High Wycombe, Bucks. Enquiries on timber drying should therefore be addressed to TRADA.

J. B. Dick
Director
Building Research Establishment
1974

Building Research Establishment
Princes Risborough Laboratory
Princes Risborough
Aylesbury
Buckinghamshire
HP 17 9PX

Acknowledgements

Grateful acknowledgements are made to the firms who kindly supplied photographs or allowed photographs of their plant to be taken and used in this manual.

Plate 5 Dehumidifiers in a forced draught timber drier
Westair Dynamics Ltd

Plate 11 Beech piled in log form in a well-kept air-seasoning yard
Goodearl-Risboro Ltd

Plate 12 Fans, steam heating pipes, spray and vents in an overhead fan kiln
Furniture Industries Ltd *G. F. Rider (Process Plants) Ltd*

Plate 13 Fan, oil-fired air heater and disc type humidifier in a side fan kiln
Goodearl-Risboro Ltd *Sidney Cubbage (Engineers) Ltd*

Plate 14 Fans and steam heating pipes in a side fan horizontal flow kiln
Shapland and Petter Ltd *G. F. Wells Ltd*

Plate 15 Battery of prefabricated side fan metal kilns
W. W. Howard Ltd *Sidney Cubbage (Engineers) Ltd*

Plate 22 Well-kept operating room
J. Gliksten & Son Ltd *G. F. Wells Ltd*

Plate 23 Aluminium carrier door
E. Gomme Ltd *G. F. Wells Ltd*

Plate 30 Lumber lift
Furniture Industries Ltd

Plate 31 Power-driven transfer car
J. Gliksten & Son Ltd *G. F. Wells Ltd*

Acknowledgements are also made to my colleagues D. D. Johnston, A. R. Dean and R. H. Wynands for their contributions to this book.

G. H. Pratt

Contents

Chapter 1
Moisture in timber

1.1 How moisture is held

All newly felled timber contains a large amount of water, most of which, for the majority of purposes, has to be removed before the wood can give satisfactory service in use. The process of seasoning is the removal of the surplus moisture as economically and with as little damage to the wood as possible.

Wood, like all plant tissue, has a cellular structure and the cells of varying shapes, sizes and arrangements are composed mainly of cellulose and lignin. The moisture in green timber is present in two forms, namely as 'free moisture' in the cell spaces and as 'bound moisture' closely associated with the substance of the cell walls. The free moisture in the growing tree is often referred to as sap. It is sometimes thought that there is more moisture present in a tree trunk during the spring and summer months than in the winter but in fact the differences observed are rarely of any practical significance.

In the seasoning of timber, sap may be regarded as being all moisture since the soluble mineral or organic substances present are small in amount and have virtually no effect on the drying properties.

1.2 What happens when wood dries

In drying, the so-called 'free' moisture in the wood cell spaces is the first to leave the wood, moving to the surfaces and evaporating from them, usually without any adverse effect on the timber. It is when the bound water leaves the cell walls that the wood substance starts to shrink and stresses and distortion develop. The point at which the cells no longer contain free moisture is called the 'fibre saturation point' and from this stage of drying, if the wood fibres are free from constraint, they will shrink to an extent which is roughly proportional to the loss in bound moisture. In practice, the surface layers of any piece of timber tend to dry to the fibre saturation point before the centre and some shrinkage of the whole will occur while the average moisture content is still relatively high. Furthermore, the surfaces, drying in advance of the interior, are brought into a state of tension and if the moisture gradient becomes too steep, splitting and checking may occur.

Wood shrinks to varying degrees along the three dimensional axes; very little along the grain in normal wood and much more across the grain. The shrinkage in the direction of the growth rings (tangentially) is often up to double that at right angles to them (radially). As a result of this, and of irregular, interlocked or spiral grain, various forms of distortion are liable to develop as a board or plank dries.

1.3 Why wood must be dried before use

Obviously it is most desirable that all the shrinkage and distortion should have taken place in timber before it is put into use and this constitutes the principal reason why wood must be dried before it can be successfully utilised. There are of course several other reasons for drying timber. For instance, most of the strength properties of timber improve when it is dried, its liability to insect and fungal attack decreases, it machines and takes finishes better and stronger glue joints can be obtained.

1.4 Moisture content of timber

1 Definition

The amount of moisture in any piece of wood is known as its moisture content. This is expressed as a percentage of the weight of dry wood in the piece, not of the total weight. Thus it is possible to have moisture contents of well over 100 per cent.

The moisture content of green wood varies greatly from one species to another. In ash, for example, it may be only 40 to 50 per cent and in the heartwood of many softwood species it is also of this order. In other woods, however, the average may be up to 150 per cent and the sapwood of softwoods is nearly always much wetter than the heartwood and may have moisture contents as high as 200 per cent (ie there is, by weight, twice as much water as there is dry wood).

2 Moisture content determination by the oven drying method

The standard method of determining the moisture content of any piece of wood is to cut a small sample from it, weigh it, dry it completely in an oven kept at 103°C ± 2°C, and then reweigh it. The loss in weight gives the amount of moisture which was in the sample when cut and the moisture content is calculated from the simple formula:

$$\text{Moisture content} = \frac{\text{Initial or wet weight} - \text{Dry weight}}{\text{Dry weight}} \times 100 \text{ per cent}$$

Suppose that the initial weight of a sample were 30·51 gm and its dry weight 22·60 gm, the difference of 7·91 gm is the weight of moisture formerly in the piece and the moisture content would be:

$$\frac{30{\cdot}51 - 22{\cdot}60}{22{\cdot}60} \times 100 = \frac{7{\cdot}91}{22{\cdot}60} \times 100 = 35{\cdot}0 \text{ per cent}$$

The formula can also be written as

$$\text{Moisture content} = \left(\frac{\text{Initial weight}}{\text{Dry weight}} - 1\right) \times 100 \text{ per cent}$$

so that in effect only the division sum need be carried out thus

$$\left(\frac{30{\cdot}51}{22{\cdot}60} - 1\right) \times 100 = 135{\cdot}0 - 100 = 35{\cdot}0 \text{ per cent}$$

In order to obtain the average moisture content of any particular board or plank it is necessary first to cut off and reject a piece at least 230 mm (9 in) from the end, for this portion will often be drier than the rest because of the more rapid drying out through the end grain. A full cross-section piece 13 mm ($\frac{1}{2}$ in) thick should then be cut from the newly sawn end and used as the sample for moisture content determination. It should be free from knots as these tend to falsify the result. To minimise waste, any piece longer than 230 mm for which there may be a use can be cut from a board before taking the cross-section sample.

Any loose slivers should be removed from the sample before weighing and the weighing should be made as quickly as possible after the sample has been cut. Errors due to unavoidable delay can be minimised by placing the samples in polythene bags immediately after cutting.

After the initial weighing the sample should be placed in a well ventilated oven maintained at a temperature of between 101 and 105°C and left there until it ceases to lose weight, showing that the drying is complete. With any particular oven and type of sample, experience will soon indicate the time taken to effect complete drying and so periodic weighing becomes unnecessary. The time will actually depend on the moisture content and species of the sample and the number of samples packed into the one oven. It may vary from about 6 to 18 hours, but results to within 1 or 2 per cent of the true moisture content can be obtained in much shorter times than these.

It may be mentioned that when a quick result is required on relatively dry wood a close approximation can be obtained in about half an hour by cutting four sections only 3 mm ($\frac{1}{8}$ in) thick, immediately weighing them all together and spacing them out in an oven containing no other samples.

Care should be taken that no fresh samples are loaded into an oven shortly before taking others out for final weighing, since the latter will temporarily gain weight owing to the uptake of moisture introduced by the wetter wood.

It should be noted that the oven drying method can give falsely high results on oily or resinous woods since the volatiles as well as the moisture may be driven off in the oven. The true moisture content of such woods can only be determined by a distillation method which requires apparatus very seldom available to those engaged in commercial timber drying. Fortunately, in the great majority of tests the results from oven drying are quite accurate enough for practical purposes, and in any case, moisture contents recommended for various uses are themselves based on values obtained from conditioned samples tested by the standard method.

Equipment required

The essential apparatus for moisture content determination by the standard method consists simply of a balance for weighing the samples and a ventilated oven in which they can be dried.

Weighing of samples

A student's chemical balance can be used and should have a capacity of about 200 gm and be capable of showing weight differences of 0·005 gm. However, in a drying plant of more than three or four kilns the amount of weighing to be done calls for the use of a more expensive semi-automatic type of balance on which weighings can be made much more rapidly. *Plate 1*. Only in circumstances when exceptionally large numbers of weighings are involved is the cost of a fully automatic balance with digital read-out likely to be justified.

Drying of samples

Any form of heated oven is suitable for drying out moisture content test samples, provided that it is well ventilated and that the temperature within it is uniform and controlled to between 101 and 105°C. *Plate 2*.

For rapid drying, when a quick answer is advantageous, infra-red ovens are available, in some of which the heating lamps are directed on to the sample on the pan of a balance incorporated in the equipment. Only one piece can be dried at a time; drying takes from about 3 to 10 minutes according to species and moisture content, and experience is needed to avoid overheating and hence inaccurate results.

3 Moisture content determination by electrical moisture meters

Moisture meters are available which can give an instantaneous indication of the moisture content of a piece of wood by measuring one of its electrical properties. The electrical resistance of wood increases rapidly with decrease in its moisture content once this is below about 25 to 30 per cent, whilst the capacity and dielectric loss decrease with fall in moisture content at all levels.

Most commercial instruments in this country, such as the one shown in Plate 3 are designed to measure the electrical resistance of a piece of wood between two needle or blade type electrodes driven into it and to interpret such a measurement in terms of moisture content on a suitably calibrated scale.

Meters have the obvious and considerable advantages that instantaneous indications of moisture content can be obtained without having to cross cut and waste some of the timber tested, they are portable so that tests can be made anywhere and no calculations are involved. Measurements can be made so rapidly and with virtually no damage to the wood that it is practicable to test large numbers of pieces from any consignment compared with only very few by the standard oven drying method. Meters would entirely displace this latter method were it not for the fact that there are a number of factors which limit their application, especially in the field of kiln drying.

Since the electrical resistance of wood changes very little above fibre saturation point, ie above about 25 to 30 per cent in most species, resistance type meters cannot give any reliable measurements of moisture content above this level (capacity and loss type meters can operate at all levels but the density of the test pieces has to be known before a close indication of the moisture content can be obtained).

The resistance at any given moisture content varies considerably, both between different species and from piece to piece within a species. As regards variation between species, meter manufacturers can meet this difficulty by incorporating a number of different scales for groups of commonly used species and supplying tables of corrections for other species. Nothing can be done about the variations within a species so that the only course is to apply an average correction and accept the fact that some divergences from oven drying test results cannot be altogether eliminated.

The electrical resistance of wood at any given moisture content decreases somewhat as the temperature increases and the effect of temperature is greater the higher the moisture content. When testing timber at moisture contents below or around 15 per cent and the temperature of the wood is known, an approximate correction for it can be made by subtracting 1 per cent from the meter reading for every 8°C above 20°C or adding 1 per cent for each 8°C below 20°C.

When timber samples are taken hot from a drying kiln it is not easy to measure the temperature of the wood between the meter electrodes and for this reason, coupled with the limited range of the instruments, the ordinary type of moisture meter cannot be relied on for gauging the progress of drying during a kiln run.

During the course of drying, the average and the core moisture contents in thick pieces of timber are appreciably higher than those in the outer zones and the ordinary type of needle electrodes cannot detect these differences as it is not practicable to push them in much deeper than 6 to 9 mm. Conversely, if dry timber becomes wet on the surfaces by exposure to a damp atmosphere or rain, the meter with ordinary electrodes will give readings much higher than the true average moisture content.

These limitations have been largely overcome by the introduction of the special type of electrode assembly illustrated in Plate 3. In this the hammer action facilitates the driving of longer and stouter pins in to a considerable depth. The pins are insulated except on the arrow head tips. The reading obtained relates to the moisture content of the wood between these tips. An indication of the moisture gradient of a test piece is obtained as the pins are driven into the wetter zones, and in the case of pieces with damp surfaces the readings are not affected by these surfaces once the pin tips penetrate below them.

The presence of certain chemicals in wood, such as the salts in preservative-treated or fire-proofed timber or the common salt in timber accidentally wetted by sea water, causes a marked lowering of its electrical resistance. Moisture meter readings taken on treated material are therefore higher than the true values, the effect on them becoming greater the higher the moisture content. The exact extent to which readings are affected depends on the particular chemicals used, on the quantity present and on the way it is distributed. It is therefore difficult to give reliable corrections for this effect; they may vary from −1 per cent to as great as −5 per cent moisture content in heavily treated zones of pieces tested at moisture contents of around 20 per cent.

In using moisture meters with ordinary needle or blade type electrodes it is important to ensure that good contact with the wood is maintained whilst the reading is taken otherwise the resistance, as measured by the meter, will be too high and the moisture content indicated will be below the true value. In practice it is not always easy to press the electrodes very far into very hard timbers, while on the other hand, with some of the softer timbers, good contact can be maintained only by keeping some pressure on the electrode holder. With the hammer type electrode assembly the risk of error due to poor contact is largely eliminated.

Despite the possible sources of error listed, electrical moisture meters remain a very useful means of finding approximate moisture contents which it is impracticable to obtain in other ways. This is particularly so where large numbers of pieces have to be tested, as in the checking and sorting of air dried material or kiln dried loads of timber.

1.5 Equilibrium moisture content

Wood is a hygroscopic material and at any time will tend to assume a moisture content which is in balance with the water vapour conditions of the surrounding atmosphere. Thus for any combination of temperature and relative humidity of the air there is a corresponding moisture content and this is termed the equilibrium moisture content (EMC). The higher the temperature or the lower the relative humidity the lower is the EMC.

The fundamental relationships between wood moisture content and air conditions have been determined by a large number of tests on commonly used species and the average EMC values are shown graphically in Figure 1. From this chart it may be seen, for example, that wood exposed to air at 15°C and 70 per cent relative humidity will tend to attain a moisture content of 15½ per cent. A rise in temperature to 20°C accompanied by a fall in relative humidity to 50 per cent would immediately result in the wood losing moisture until a new equilibrium is established; this would be at a moisture content of approximately 11 per cent. Conversely a rise in humidity or a fall in temperature or both would cause the wood to absorb moisture.

It must be emphasised that the EMC curves shown depict only average values and that the EMC of any particular piece of timber is affected by a number of factors such as its species and its previous history.

Certain species, such as teak and afrormosia, have EMC values that are from 2 to 3 per cent below the average of all species and even in one species the variation exhibited by individual samples may be quite marked.

The curves in Figure 1 have been drawn from data obtained from test specimens during a drying cycle. Had the wood first been dried to a moisture content corresponding with a low humidity and allowed to absorb moisture and come into equilibrium with air at higher humidities, values about 2 per cent lower would have been obtained throughout. This phenomenon is referred to as hysteresis and the desorption and absorption curves drawn on the same axes of a graph form what is known as a hysteresis loop.

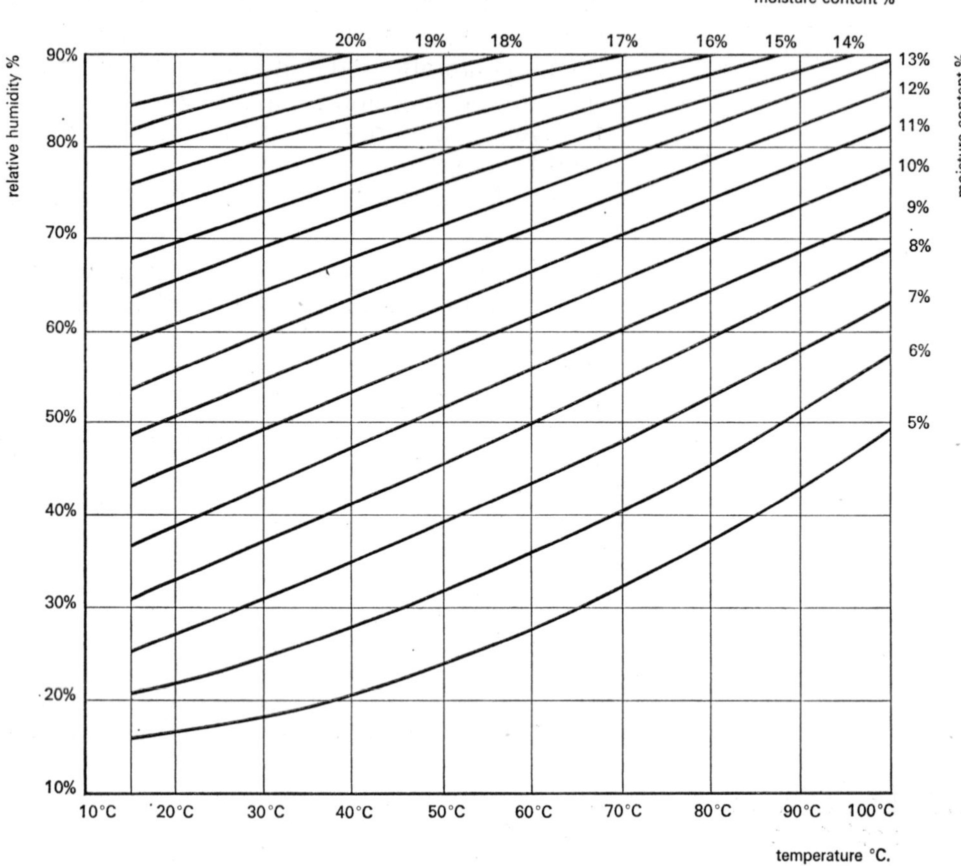

Figure 1 *Chart showing the relationship between the moisture content of wood and the temperature and relative humidity of the surrounding air*

The EMC values of wood dried from green at high temperatures or subjected to a steaming treatment are lower by 1 or 2 per cent moisture content than those of air dried material and this fact partly accounts for the lower EMC of plywood compared with ordinary wood.

1.6 Moisture content of timber in use

It follows from the previous section that any wooden article or component will tend to assume a moisture content corresponding with the average temperature and humidity of the air to which it is exposed, provided of course that it is protected from wetting or sunlight.

Daily fluctuations in air conditions will not greatly affect the average moisture content of any item unless it is thin or has a high proportion of end grain. Seasonal variations however, such as are found in the UK both out-of-doors and in dwelling houses, offices, etc, have a considerable effect on moisture content and produce changes in dimension and sometimes shape which vary with the species of the wood in question.

The moisture content in stacks of timber under cover but exposed to outdoor atmospheric conditions will vary from 22 to 23 in winter to about 16 to 17 in good summer weather.

In heated buildings during winter, however, the rise in temperature results in a fall in relative humidity and both result in moisture contents in joinery and furniture as low as from 9 to 11 per cent depending on the degree of heating. In spring and autumn months with no heating, moisture contents may be of the order of 13 to 14 per cent.

Moisture contents likely to be found in various items can be estimated if the atmospheric conditions they will encounter are known but the values shown in the diagram in Figure 2 have been determined largely from actual tests for moisture content in articles in use.

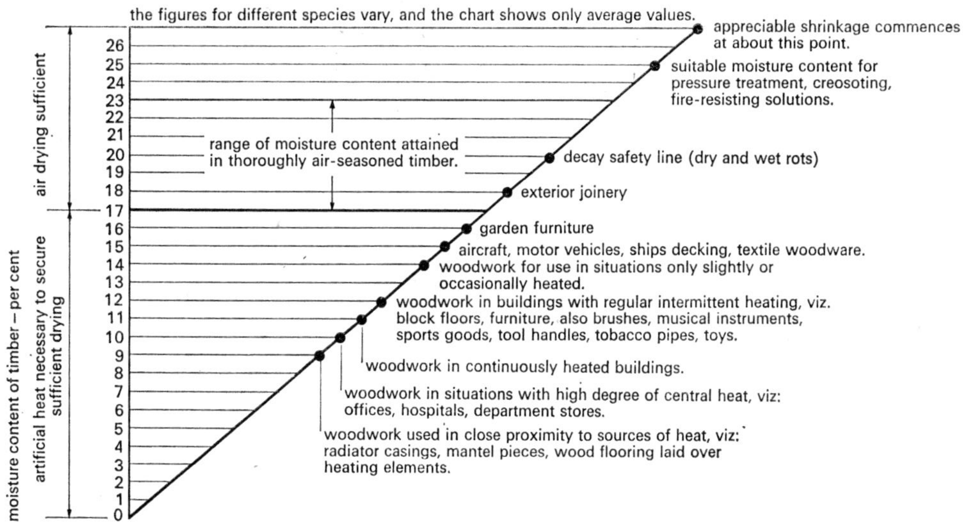

Figure 2 *Moisture contents of timber in various environments*

1 Moisture content specification

Ideally, the moisture content to which timber should be dried before it is machined and used is the average or somewhat below the average of what the item will attain in use. It is not always essential that this should be done, however, and moisture content specifications for building components, for instance, take this into account. The structural parts of a house such as roof members, carcassing, etc, can dry out further *in situ* to some extent without the accompanying shrinkage and distortion having any serious effects. For hardwood flooring, doors, furniture, etc, it is necessary to specify moisture contents close to those which will obtain in use if a satisfactory result is to be achieved. It is usual to specify an average moisture content and to state the variation which can be tolerated, about ±2 per cent moisture content in most cases. An instance of this is to be seen in the British Standard 1186 : 1971, in which the moisture content clause states:

'The moisture content of the timber during manufacture and when the joinery is handed over to the purchaser shall be within plus or minus two of the average equilibrium moisture content per cent that it is expected to attain in service and which shall be specified by the purchaser as follows:

1 External joinery

External joinery to heated or unheated buildings — *17%*

2 Internal joinery

- *a Buildings with intermittent heating* — *15%*
- *b Buildings with continuous heating providing room temperature in the range 12 to 18°C* — *12%*
- *c Buildings with continuous heating providing room temperature in the range 20 to 24°C* — *10%*
- *d Close proximity to sources of heat* — *8%*

Note: *Where a moisture meter is used to establish the moisture content the test shall be carried out according to the instrument manufacturer's instructions at a point not nearer than 600 mm from either end, or at the centre if the length is less than 1200 mm.'*

In kiln plants operated by manufacturers to supply timber correctly dried for their products, the management should specify the moisture content condition required and should take steps to ensure that it is obtained. Moisture meters can be used for this purpose. Similarly, customers should make checks on the moisture content of timber they receive from 'public driers'.

In the case of timber merchants drying for stock, the exact end use for the kiln dried timber is often not known and in the absence of heated storage facilities it is usual to dry the loads to moisture contents of about 15 ± 3 per cent.

Chapter 2 Methods of drying

2.1 General principles involved in timber drying

Over the years many methods of drying timber have been tried but very few of them have proved fully successful in the sense that drying can be achieved at reasonable cost and without detriment to the timber.

Only small quantities of liquid water can be removed by purely mechanical means such as centrifuging or passing between pressure rollers, and flushing out the moisture with a water-miscible organic solvent (eg acetone) is a satisfactory method for only a few wood species.

The most common method is to extract moisture in the form of water vapour and heat must be supplied to the wood to provide the latent heat of evaporation. There are different ways in which this essential heat may be conveyed to the wood and in which the water vapour is conducted away.

Nearly all the world's timber is in fact dried in air, either at ordinary atmospheric temperatures (air drying) or in a kiln or drier at controlled temperatures raised artificially above atmospheric temperature but not usually above 100°C, the boiling point of water (conventional kiln drying). It is important to realise that air drying and kiln drying are fundamentally the same method in that air is the medium which both conveys heat to the wood and carries away the evaporated moisture.

1 Factors influencing the drying of wood in air

There are five major factors which influence the drying of wood in air.

1.1 Vapour pressure and relative humidity

For a full understanding of how wood dries in air it is desirable to introduce the terms vapour pressure and relative humidity. When air holds the maximum possible amount of vapour the vapour exerts what is called the saturation vapour pressure. If the water vapour present is less than this maximum then the air is capable of taking up more moisture. The ratio of actual vapour pressure to the saturation vapour pressure at any given temperature, expressed as a percentage, is called the relative humidity (rh).

When a piece of wet wood is exposed to air which is not already saturated (ie its relative humidity is less than 100 per cent) evaporation takes place from its surfaces. The rate of evaporation is dependent on the difference between the vapour pressure exerted by the wet wood surfaces and that of the air/water vapour mixture in immediate contact with them.

1.2 Supply of heat

When timber dries it is cooled by the evaporation of the moisture and heat can then pass to it from the warmer ambient air, thus supplying the latent heat of evaporation essential for the continuation of drying. The vapour pressure exerted by the wood gradually falls as it gets drier, and so the rate of evaporation decreases, the temperature of the wood rises nearer to that of the circulating air and less heat is transferred to the wood. Some idea of the heat required when drying large quantities of wood may be gained from the fact that drying say 15 m^3 (530 cu ft) from the green condition to 20 per cent moisture content can involve the evaporation of 4500 kg of water and if heat is supplied electrically the consumption could amount to well over 3000 kW h.

In air drying, the necessary heat costs nothing for it is supplied by air which, having directly or indirectly derived heat from the sun, gives up some of it as it passes over the timber, the amount depending on the relative humidity, the speed of the air and the moisture content of the timber surfaces.

In a kiln, the air circulated through the timber stack is heated as it first passes over some form of heat source, such as steam heating pipes. Most of the air is re-circulated and re-heated but some has to be exhausted through ventilators to carry away the moisture taken up from the timber. Heat is therefore required to warm up the cool air drawn in to replace the air exhausted and some further heat must be supplied to make good the losses through the shell of the drying chamber. The total heat requirements of a ventilated kiln are thus in excess of the heat needed solely to evaporate the moisture from the timber.

1.3 Air movement

If the air surrounding a piece of wet wood is stagnant and limited in quantity, then it will soon tend to become saturated and evaporation of moisture from the wood will virtually cease.

Even when there is a continuous stream of air passing over the wood the film of air in immediate contact with the wood will move more slowly and have a higher vapour pressure than the main stream. This is known as 'the boundary layer effect' and the greater the velocity of the main stream the less is the effect, especially as the flow becomes turbulent instead of laminar, and the faster is the rate of evaporation. An increase in air speed can therefore be regarded as equivalent to a reduction in the 'effective' humidity near the wood surfaces.

Since air in passing through a stack of wet wood both gives up heat and takes up moisture it is bound to be cooler and more humid where it emerges than where it enters and the drying rate is therefore slower on the air outlet than on the air inlet side. The faster the air speed and the narrower the stack the smaller is the difference between the two sides and for this reason fairly high air speeds are desirable in a drying kiln, particularly when the timber being dried is very wet and parts readily with its moisture. The uniformity of drying can be further improved by reversing the direction of air flow through the kiln stack at regular intervals (see 5.0).

1.4 Movement of moisture within the wood

When moisture evaporates from the surface of a piece of wet wood the moisture concentration in the outer layers is lowered and moisture begins to move from the wetter interior to the drier surfaces. For the consideration of practical drying it will suffice to accept the movement as being a combination of capillary flow and vapour diffusion. The structure of wood offers resistance to the passage of moisture and in some species, especially in dense hardwoods such as oak, greenheart, jarrah, etc, this resistance is very considerable. If the evaporation from the surfaces occurs at a faster rate than the moisture from the interior zones flows to these surfaces, the moisture gradient within the wood becomes progressively steeper. As the outer layers dry below the fibre saturation point their tendency to start shrinking is resisted by the wetter interior so that a state of stress develops, with the outer layers in tension and the inner zones in compression. If the stresses become too severe the outer layers may rupture ie surface checking may occur, or they may become stretched beyond the elastic limit without breaking and the wood is then said to be casehardened.

In both air and kiln drying the establishment of a reasonable moisture gradient is unavoidable and indeed desirable, for in any particular piece of wood at a given temperature the rate of movement of moisture up to the surface is proportional to the steepness of the gradient. The skill in timber drying really lies in allowing the gradient to become as steep as the wood will tolerate without suffering damage, and in controlling the rate of evaporation to match the rate at which moisture is reaching the surface.

1.5 The influence of temperature on drying rate

When a moisture gradient has been set up following surface drying, the difference in vapour pressure between core and surface may be regarded as the driving force causing the outward movement of moisture. The vapour pressure exerted by water or by wood containing water rises very rapidly with increasing temperature and the rate of increase itself is greater the higher the moisture content of the wood.

To illustrate the effect of temperature on drying rate it can be estimated that in a piece of wood having a surface moisture content of 16 per cent and a core moisture content of 40 per cent, the vapour pressure gradient across the wood at a temperature of 50°C is four times greater than that at 20°C and at 80°C it is more than eight times as large. The results of experiments on the kiln drying of Sitka spruce are shown graphically in Figure 3.

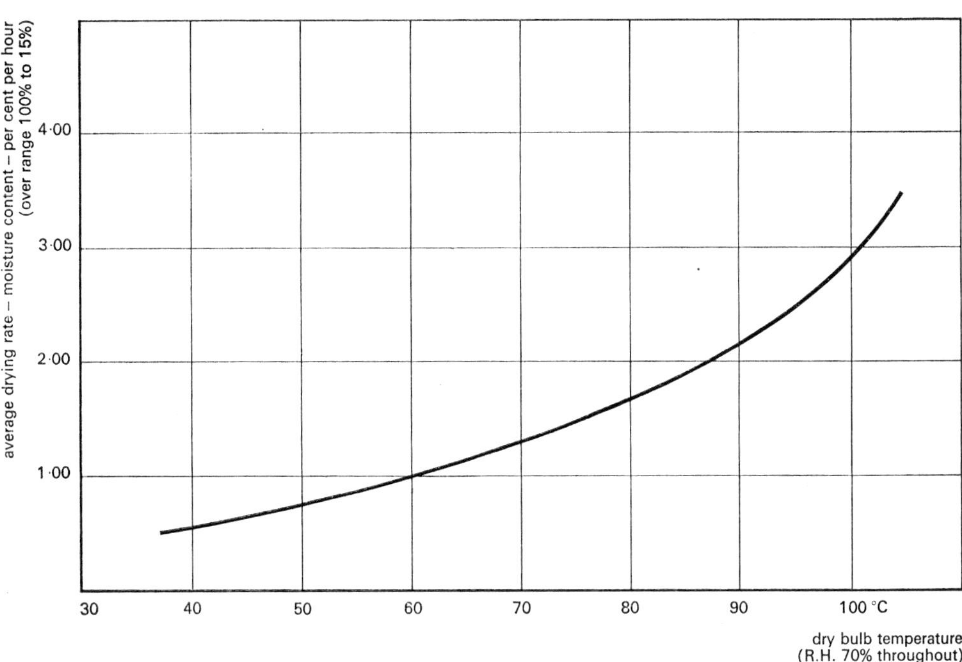

Figure 3 *Effect of temperature on rate of drying of 25 mm Sitka spruce*

In kiln drying, there are further advantages in the use of high temperatures in that the capacity of air for holding water vapour, and hence its drying potential, increases rapidly with temperature and the amount of air which has to be exhausted, and hence the heat lost in this way, is reduced. Furthermore the rate at which a load can be conditioned to obtain a reasonably uniform final moisture content is increased.

Unfortunately the considerable benefits obtainable by raising the temperature at which wood is dried cannot always be fully realised because there are limits to the temperatures which various species will tolerate without detriment.

In the drying of many species, especially medium and heavy hardwoods, shrinkage and hence distortion increase as the drying temperature is raised and with species which are particularly prone to distort, such as elm, it is necessary to employ comparatively low temperatures. A few species are liable to collapse and/or honeycomb (see 3.2, 3.5) if dried at high temperatures, many tend to darken appreciably and in resinous timbers, drying at temperatures above about 50°C causes the resin to exude on to the wood surfaces. Although this is not necessarily detrimental for many products it is often considered by the users to be objectionable. Finally, since high temperature drying may cause a slight loss in impact strength, it is advisable to limit the temperature to about 60°C when drying timber for items such as tool handles, sports goods etc.

2.2 General comparison between air drying and kiln drying

Air drying
The main differences between air drying and kiln drying will be obvious from the foregoing outline of the theory of timber drying. In air drying, the timber is subjected to all the vagaries of the local climate and there is virtually no control of the temperature, relative humidity or speed of the air passing through the timber stacks. The rate of drying can thus vary from nil on a calm, damp day to quite fast enough to cause surface checking during spells of dry, windy weather.

Owing to the comparatively low temperature and high humidity conditions prevailing in the United Kingdom, air drying is a slow process during most months of the year. Times taken to reach 20 to 25 per cent moisture content vary from 2 or 3 months to 1 or 2 years, depending of course upon the species and size of the timber. It is also impossible to dry timber below the EMC of the atmosphere so that, except in unusually hot, dry weather, the lowest moisture content obtainable is around 16 to 17 per cent, whilst in the winter months, even under full cover, wood will not come down to much lower than 22 to 23 per cent. It is quite obvious, therefore, that air drying alone is not sufficient for bringing timber into a fit state for most interior uses where it will eventually attain average moisture contents of between 8 and 12 per cent.

Kiln drying
In contrast to air drying conditions, in a modern drying kiln a steady and adequate flow of air through the timber stacks is promoted by fans and the condition of this air can be controlled to any desired schedule levels of temperature and relative humidity to suit the species and sizes of timber being dried. It is thus possible to make full use of the increase in drying rate obtainable by raising the temperature to the maximum values which the particular timber has been found by laboratory experiment and trade experience to accept without excessive degrade. At the same time, the relative humidity can be controlled so that the moisture gradients set up in the wood are not quite so steep as to cause surface checking.

In addition to the advantages of speed of drying and limitation of degrade, kiln drying makes it possible to bring the timber to any desired moisture content appropriate to its ultimate use.

The direct costs of kiln drying are much higher than those of air drying for they include charges on the capital equipment and the cost of fuel, electricity and supervision. These are partially or more than wholly offset by the big reduction in the quantity of stock needed and the time it has to be held; kilning times being anything from about one tenth to one thirtieth of those for air drying. A method of estimating the drying times for various species and sizes is given in Appendix B.

1 Air drying followed by kiln drying
The cost per day of running a kiln is such that kiln drying tends to become uneconomical when the species and size of timber being dried demand long kiln treatments. Thus, with material taking more than about 4 or 5 weeks to kiln dry from green it will often be found more economical to air dry first down to about 25 to 30 per cent moisture content and then to complete the drying in a kiln.

The economic advantage of this procedure may sometimes be lost, however, if the layout or lack of handling facilities necessitates dismantling the air dried stack and repiling the timber for kiln drying. It must also be realised that with some difficult species the amount of splitting and checking which occurs when they are air dried in summer months may be excessive.

2.3 Other methods using air as the drying medium

1 Forced air drying
In so-called 'forced air drying' fans are erected alongside ordinary air drying stacks to promote a steady flow of air through them. *Plate 4.* This does result in faster drying in periods of calm, relatively dry weather, especially when fresh sawn timber is first put in stick.

Trials carried out at the Princes Risborough Laboratory have indicated that, in UK conditions, the overall reductions in drying times achieved by this method are seldom likely to be sufficient to offset the cost of providing and running the necessary fan systems. In the first place, weather conditions in this country are such that the periods when there is no wind to cause movements of air in the stacks are comparatively short and rare. Secondly, the temperatures and relative humidities prevailing for long periods, especially at night, correspond to high EMC values, so that little worthwhile drying can be achieved whether there is a good air speed through the stacks or not. To save waste of power, instruments (humidistats) can be used to shut off the fans whenever the relative humidity rises above say 90 to 95 per cent, but the net result is still of doubtful advantage in normal circumstances. An exception might be found in the rare cases when air drying has to be done where only limited space is available and the yard is protected from normal wind currents. It is obvious, however, that no amount of increased air flow can bring the wood to a moisture content lower than that related to the ordinary atmosphere, viz between 17 and 23 per cent, according to the time of year.

2 Accelerated air drying
By heating the air blown through the timber stacks its relative humidity is lowered and hence its drying potential is increased, and both faster drying and lower moisture contents can be achieved. This process is sometimes called accelerated air drying as distinct from air drying and forced air drying, in which no extra heat is supplied. In effect, an attempt is made to maintain good drying conditions throughout the year.

There are three drawbacks to the method:

1 The temperature cannot be raised much above that of the ambient air for an increase of only 10°C will lower the relative humidity by around 30 per cent and species liable to surface check would then tend to suffer damage.

2 The amount of heat added to the air blown through the stacks has to be controlled to prevent wide fluctuations in relative humidity resulting from night to day variations and from changes from damp to dry weather periods.

3 The air is not recirculated, so that unless the stacks are wide the air leaves them whilst still warm and at comparatively low humidities and drying potential is wasted. On the other hand, if the length of travel is increased so that the emerging air is virtually saturated, a considerable difference in drying rate is bound to exist from one side of the stack to the other.

3 Pre-drying

The term 'pre-drying' is applied to the procedure adopted, mainly in Australia and to a lesser extent in America, for the drying of refractory hardwoods from green to around 20 to 30 per cent moisture content prior to completion of the drying in a conventional kiln.

The drying is carried out in large (200 to 1000 m^3 timber capacity), low-cost buildings equipped with fans and heating, the air being re-circulated and the humidity controlled mainly by automatic adjustment of the vents. Operating temperatures are of the order of 40 to 45°C.

The cost of the pre-driers is low per unit volume of timber accommodated—around a half to a third of that in conventional kilns—and because air conditions in them are kept relatively mild, loads of various species and sizes can be dried simultaneously.

With rare exceptions, it is considered that, under conditions operating in the United Kingdom, the overall economic benefits of pre-drying over ordinary air drying are small and unlikely to lead to the adoption of the method.

4 Drying in climate chambers

Climate chambers are large enclosed buildings with very slow natural air circulation; air interchange is brought about by temperature and vapour pressure differences. In effect they are improved versions of the air drying or conditioning rooms used in the past. Like pre-driers they are run at relatively mild and constant conditions, the temperature being limited to around 40°C. Below this level the actual temperature is controlled through a humidistat to produce relative humidities of the order of 50 to 55 per cent.

The drying is inevitably slower than in the pre-driers with their forced air circulation but final moisture contents of 10 to 12 per cent can be attained and species and thicknesses can be mixed so that small loads of timber can be moved into and out of the chamber as required. Climate chambers, developed in Holland, are used mainly for material which is naturally slow drying due to its species and/or thickness. They are said to be economic because of the very low capital cost per unit timber volume, the low heat losses and the reduction to a minimum of any necessary supervision.

5 Dehumidifier drying

The basic principle in drying with the aid of dehumidifiers is still that of exposing timber to air kept at controllable levels of temperature and humidity. The main difference from drying in climate rooms, pre-driers or kilns is that the moisture evaporated from the timber load is removed from the drying chamber, not by air interchange through vents, but by dehumidifying equipment. When this is of the refrigeration type the moisture is condensed on the cold coils and the latent heat otherwise lost in the moisture passing out through the vents is recovered and the thermal efficiency of the drying process is thereby considerably increased.

In the simplest use of dehumidifiers for timber drying, one or more dehumidifiers are introduced into a closed, well-insulated chamber which is maintained at a temperature of 20 to 30°C and a relative humidity of about 40 to 50 per cent, the latter being controlled by switching the dehumidifier on and off through a humidistat. Such driers are used mainly for bringing mixed loads of timber down from an air dried or partially air dried condition to 10 to 12 per cent moisture content.

In other applications, the dehumidifier units are placed either within, or in chambers alongside, the air passages in conventional kilns with forced air circulation. *Plate 5.* Kiln humidities to suit each particular load are applied by adjustment of a humidistat but the temperature employed must be kept within the range of 20°C to 55°C within which the dehumidifiers function efficiently. Therefore, full advantage cannot be taken of the increase in drying rate obtainable in kilns with ordinary heating and ventilation, on species of timber which will tolerate much higher temperatures.

Other methods of drying timber

A brief description of drying methods which do not use air as the drying medium will be found in Chapter 11. They include such processes as radio frequency heating, vacuum drying and 'chemical seasoning'.

Chapter 3
Degrade during drying

Almost all forms of seasoning degrade are attributable to the fact that wood shrinks in drying. Since some shrinkage is bound to occur it follows that just as some volumetric loss is inevitable, so certain other forms of degrade must also be accepted as very liable to accompany the drying process.

It is possible, however, to minimise some forms of degrade, such as distortion, and to avoid others, by adopting correct drying techniques. This applies far more in kiln drying, with its controlled air conditions, than in air drying.

In Appendix E the various defects which may develop during kiln drying are summarised and indications given as to how they may be avoided or reduced to a minimum.

3.1 Checking and splitting

In kiln and air seasoning, moisture evaporates from the board surfaces and if this evaporation rate is in excess of the rate of moisture transfusion from the centre, a moisture gradient is induced with the board surfaces at a lower moisture content than the centre. Some such gradient is unavoidable, and indeed necessary, if drying is to proceed, but should it become very steep, the outer parts of the wood will tend to shrink excessively on to the inner, and severe stresses will develop. The stresses so induced may become great enough to tear the outer fibres apart and thus cause surface checking. *Plate 6*.

Since the shrinkage in the direction of the growth rings is greater than that at right angles to them, checking is most likely to occur mainly on the faces of tangentially cut boards and on the edges of quarter-sawn material, usually along the rays, which form planes of weakness. Wood is more prone to suffer this defect during the early stages of drying, when it is green and when moisture gradients may be considerable, than during the later stages when the material is at a lower moisture content throughout.

The fact that planks are very liable to check on the ends and to develop splits there may be attributed to the relative ease with which moisture moves in the longitudinal direction and out of the ends. Zones near the ends of boards thus have a tendency to dry and shrink in advance of the remainder. This tendency may lead to stresses sufficient to cause end splits to develop and to extend an appreciable distance along the board. Splitting and checking can be minimised, if not entirely eliminated, by controlling the air conditions in such a way as to ensure that the rate of moisture evaporation from the surfaces is not excessive. It will be observed that in the recommended drying schedules given in Appendix B, which are mostly based on experience gained in the seasoning of the various timbers, the relative humidity of the air is kept comparatively high in the early stages of the treatment. In this way the surface drying rate is limited sufficiently to prevent the development of moisture gradients, and hence stressing, great enough to cause damage to the material. It must be borne in mind, however, that the quality of the timber, and any previous treatment, may have a bearing on its tendency to split and that the operator should keep a careful watch on the timber so as to determine whether the recommended conditions are, in fact, suitable for the particular load, or whether, for example, a humidity increase with the object of minimising the degrade from splitting and checking is advisable. It is not always possible to prevent the ends from splitting from the causes given above, and boards and planks are usually cut rather longer than required so as to allow for this somewhat prevalent defect.

In the seasoning of special high quality dimension stock, such as oak furniture squares, it is uneconomical to add appreciably to the lengths to allow for wastage from end checking and splitting and it is customary to seal the ends with a moisture-resistant paint or wax, so that end drying will be restricted and splitting thereby eliminated or much reduced. From the aspects of reduction of end checking and splitting, the end coating of boards is to be recommended, but such a procedure is normally ruled out on the score of added labour and expense.

End cleats attached to boards or planks in order to prevent them splitting after conversion or on exposure to the sun during air drying are of doubtful value in kiln drying. If the cleats are rigid, strong and firmly nailed to the ends of the timber they may, by restraining the natural shrinkage, actually cause end splits to develop or extend and they should therefore be removed before kiln drying is begun.

Naturally an operator must take every precaution to ensure that the treatment he applies results in the least possible damage to the timber, but obviously he cannot eliminate any defects, such as splits and shakes, which are present in the material when he receives it. For example, it is quite common to find that oak to be kiln dried after preliminary air drying has already checked badly, and, what is more, the checks may have closed up to such an extent as to be invisible. These defects soon make themselves apparent again on further drying and the most that can be done is to keep them from extending, and even this is difficult. An attempt to close the checks by steaming or the use of a very high humidity may possibly be successful for a time, but when the surface re-dries, they will, in all probability, be larger than before.

Box-hearted material, particularly that containing heartshake, is almost certain to open up and suffer degrade despite care taken in seasoning and, so far as is possible, such material should be excluded from the load.

3.2 Honeycombing

Stressed wood need not necessarily split since the initially stretched outer and compressed inner zones may yield a certain amount one to another. Should this yield not exceed the elastic limit, no harm results, but should the elastic limit be passed, 'permanent set' or deformation tends to develop (see casehardening, 3.4).

The outer zone will tend to 'set' in an expanded condition and the inner will tend to 'set' in compression. These sets, if they persist, will tend to reduce and increase respectively the ultimate shrinkage of the two zones. This implies that when the centre parts dry below the fibre saturation point they will tend to shrink in excess of and be resisted by the expanded outer zones. Stressing will again develop, but now in the opposite sense with the centre in tension and the surface in compression. Should these stresses become large, the stretched fibres of the centre may be torn apart and splits formed inside the material. *Plate 7.* Internal splitting of this sort is usually referred to as honeycombing, and is rather deceptive since its development is often not suspected from superficial examination. Its presence is occasionally indicated by slight caving in on the tangential faces.

From what has been said it is clear that honeycombing can usually be avoided by ensuring that heavy stressing does not develop during the early stages of drying and by applying special casehardening relief treatments (see 9.6).

It may be mentioned here that what often appears to be honeycombing in certain woods, notably oak, may, in fact, be surface checking or splitting that has developed during the early stages of drying and has penetrated deeply into the timber. During the final stages, when the surface layers are in compression, these splits may close so tightly near the surfaces as to become invisible from the outside, but, upon cross-cutting, they appear as internal checks or honeycombing.

3.3 Distortion

Much of the distortion that occurs during drying results from the fact that wood does not shrink equally in all directions. For example, the shrinkage in the direction of the growth rings is often about double that of the shrinkage in the radial direction, and this results in a tendency for a plain-sawn board to 'cup' in drying. A cross-section of a plain-sawn board cupped as a result of differential shrinkage is illustrated in Figure 4. It will be noted that the board has curved in the opposite direction to the curvature of the rings. The reason for this is that the under face, being nearer the heart of the tree than the upper face, is more nearly radial and so tends to shrink by a rather smaller amount. The greater shrinkage of the top face has led to a curvature away from the heart, and distortion has resulted. From similar reasoning, it may be shown that twist, bow and spring *Fig 4* may be attributable to differential shrinkage in boards containing distorted or curved grain. Differential shrinkage is also responsible for distortions in and around knots and for the 'diamonding' of squared material not cut on the quarter. *Fig 4.*

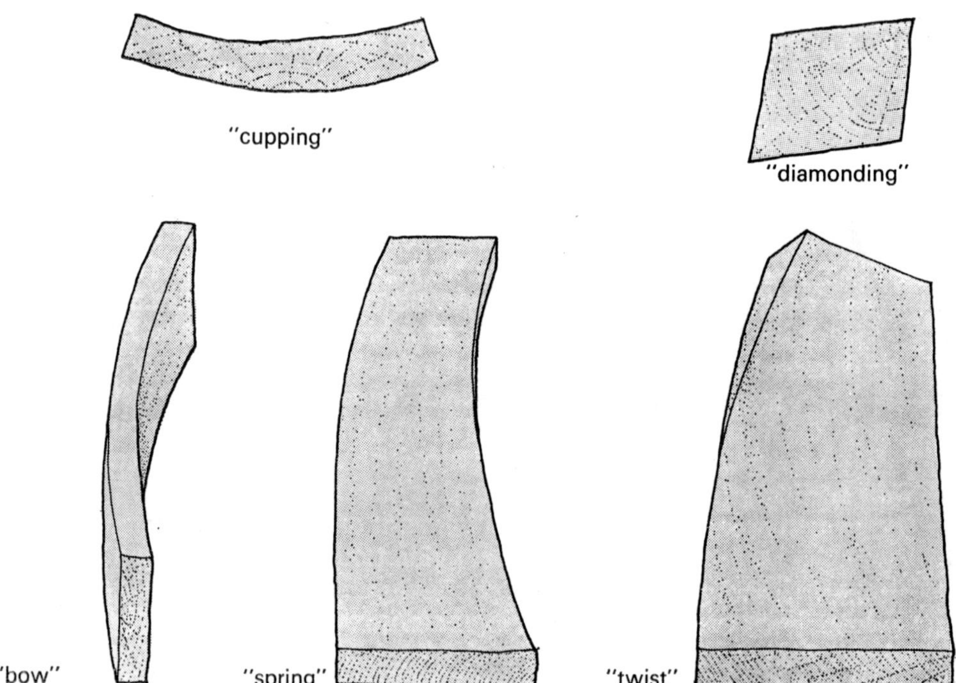

Figure 4 *Various forms of distortion; cross-sectional and longitudinal*

Normally the shrinkage of timber along the grain is very small and may be treated as negligible in most cases. Certain woods, however, contain zones of reaction wood (compression or tension wood) which shrink appreciably along the length, occasionally as much as 1 or 2 per cent. Such shrinkage often results in excessive longitudinal distortion either during drying or when subsequently re-sawing to thickness or width.

Poor quality material, and woods such as elm in which the grain direction is seldom straight, have a marked tendency to distort, and these need to be piled very carefully and in some instances weighted down in order to reduce distortion to a minimum. The underlying principle here is that the boards or planks should be held down in their horizontal layers in a manner best calculated to resist any tendency to distort. Wood, being a semi-plastic material, particularly at kiln temperatures, will yield somewhat to the restraining forces, and much if not all of the distortion may be eliminated. In some instances this may be accomplished only at the expense of some increase in splitting, but generally this is far outweighed by the overall improvement in shape.

Conversely, it follows that as a result of faulty piling with bad alignment of sticks set at wide intervals, even straight grained, good quality material may become distorted in the warm kiln conditions.

Tests have indicated that high temperatures, apart from making wood more plastic, tend also to increase the shrinkage and so increase distortions, especially in the case of many hardwoods. For this reason, comparatively low temperature drying schedules are recommended for woods that are prone to distort badly in seasoning.

3.4 Casehardening

Casehardening may be defined as the condition existing in timber which results from drying stresses and the strains they induce; the surface layers having become set in an expanded condition they are finally under compression whilst the interior is in tension. The term casehardening, though universally accepted for timber in this condition, is an unfortunate and somewhat misleading one for neither the hardness nor the permeability of wood is materially affected by its being under stress.

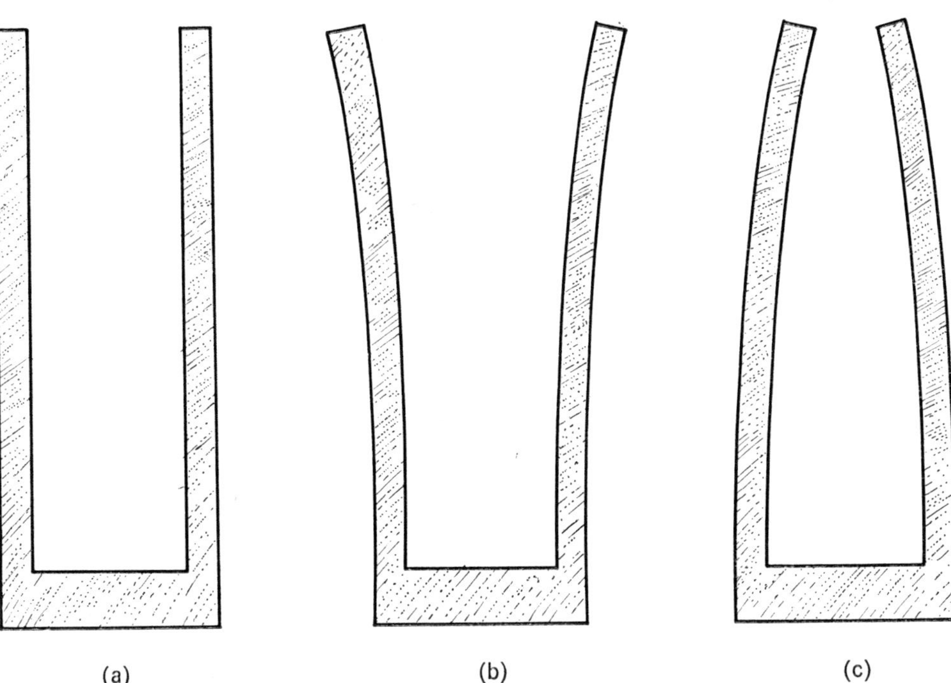

Figure 5 *Casehardening test prongs*

In the early stages of drying the surfaces of a piece of wood tend to lose moisture at a faster rate than the centre. Inevitably, therefore, there is a tendency for the outer layers to shrink in advance of the interior with the result that compressive stresses develop in the interior and tensile stresses in and near the surfaces. These stresses produce corresponding strains, the outer layers becoming stretched and the inner layers compressed by an amount depending on the magnitude of the forces that develop. So long as the strains never exceed the elastic limit of the particular piece of wood no trouble will arise, since, when a uniform moisture content is finally reached, no part of the cross-section will tend to be longer or shorter than similar parts adjacent to it. When the strains increase beyond the elastic limit, however, 'permanent sets' may develop which lead to the casehardening of the timber.

The existence and intensity of casehardening stresses can be determined by cutting cross-sections about 12 mm thick not less than 200 mm from one end of the piece under test and cutting out the centre portion to within about 25 mm of one end leaving a prong shaped test piece as in Figure 5a. When such test prongs are cut there is usually a moisture content gradient across the piece and, whilst their behaviour immediately on cutting indicates the stresses present, the prongs must be left to dry out to a uniform moisture content by leaving them exposed in a room for about 24 hours in order to determine the strains resulting from them.

Prongs newly cut from a plank in the early stages of drying will at first curve outwards as in Figure 5b but as they dry to a uniform moisture content they will either come back straight if no permanent set has developed or, if this has developed, they will finally curve inward as in Figure 5c.

As the drying of a board or plank continues and the inner portions dry and try to shrink by the normal amount, there is a gradual changeover in the distribution of stress, the core coming into tension and the outer shell into compression. Test prongs cut from wood in this condition will immediately curve inwards and the curvature will increase if the centre was wetter than the outside when cut.

Prongs cut from heavily casehardened material will tend to spring inward on the saw and press tightly together after conditioning in the room. The prongs from timber in which the stresses are small may be straight on cutting and become slightly curved later.

The way in which the stresses in casehardened timber can be balanced and relieved in a drying kiln by administering a high temperature, high humidity treatment is described in section 9.6.

If too drastic a relief treatment is given, reverse casehardening can result and this condition produces the only occasion on which test prongs spring outwards on cutting and remain curved outward even when uniformly dry.

Boards containing casehardening stresses may be flat and have no apparent degrade but if they are deep-sawn or heavily machined the balance of stress within the material is disturbed and some distortion, mainly 'cup', will almost certainly result.

A word of warning must be given here against the deep sawing of partly dried planks followed by the kiln drying of the boards so produced. If the surfaces have been stressed beyond the elastic limit it will be impossible to remedy the cupping that occurs with deep sawing and indeed this will get worse as the freshly exposed damper surface of each board dries and shrinks more than the original surface.

3.5 Collapse

Collapse is yet another form of distortion to which some timbers are prone, notably certain species of *Eucalyptus*. A board of 'Tasmanian oak', for example, if dried at high or even moderate temperatures, is very liable to distort or collapse in the manner illustrated in Plate 8. Collapse occurs during the early stages of drying when the free moisture leaves the cells, and it is brought about by the surface tension forces which this moisture exerts upon the cell walls, causing them to be pulled inwards and to collapse. Rapid drying at high temperatures may cause the semi-plastic cells to collapse to a very large extent and under these conditions even certain home-grown woods such as elm may be affected. Local shrinkages may become large, and frequently the deformations lead to severe internal checking or honeycombing.

It has been found that, in many instances, much of the collapse and consequent distortion may be removed when the wood is nearly dry by means of a high temperature steaming treatment, usually referred to as reconditioning (see 10.1).

3.6 Staining and discoloration

Staining and discoloration sometimes occur during the kiln drying of timber and may become objectionable if, as a result, the wood is unevenly or unpleasantly coloured and if the stains cannot readily be removed by planing. Staining may be caused by the growth of fungi or by chemical changes in the wood, and although precise knowledge of the nature of the latter and of definite means of preventing the staining is lacking, the information given below should be of some help to the operator who encounters this form of degrade.

1 Stains caused by fungi

In certain timbers stains develop, principally in the sapwood, owing to the growth of fungi of the mould type. Blue stain in softwoods is a well known example of this but some light-coloured hardwoods are also likely to become stained in a similar manner. With any timber subject to staining, care should be taken to avoid delay between conversion and kiln drying as the bulk piling of green timber provides ideal conditions for development of infection. Furthermore, for the avoidance of staining and to obtain uniformity of colour, all sawdust should be brushed off boards and planks before they are piled for seasoning.

With softwoods, the high temperatures used and the rapid drying achieved in a kiln prevent the development of sap-stain, but with stain-susceptible species dried at temperatures insufficiently high to arrest mould growth, special treatments should be given as prescribed in section 10.3.

The 'Golden Oak' fungus, which causes the yellow stain occasionally found in oak and sweet chestnut, is less easy to control. The low temperature and high humidity conditions necessary in the early stages of the drying of these species actually encourage the growth of the fungus. Dipping or spraying with an antiseptic solution immediately after conversion will check the development of the stain. Alternatively, an initial steaming of the green timber at 100°C (212°F) will free the load from infection but such a steaming will tend to darken the timber permanently.

2 Staining and discoloration caused by chemical changes in the wood

1 *Uniform change of colour.* Most woods darken in colour to varying degrees owing to the use of elevated temperatures during kiln drying. Frequently the discoloration is due to oxidation of some constituents of the wood substance and at temperatures such as those used in Schedules H, J, K, L and M (*Appendix B*) darkening is also caused by the combined effect of temperature and moisture (hydrolysis) on the wood.

In certain species, of which sycamore is a notable example, a general discoloration occurs throughout the timber even when it is kiln dried at moderate temperatures (eg Schedule E), and this is thought to be due to changes brought about by the action of enzymes in the wood. If it is desired to preserve a light colour, the wood must be dried at lower temperatures than those given in the standard schedules, which are devised mainly, of course, to minimise checking and distortion. Sycamore, for example, should be dried to Schedule A instead of Schedule E.

2 *Stick stain*. On dismantling piles of certain species of timber after seasoning it is sometimes found that where the piling sticks have been in contact with the wood there are distinct bands different in colour from the rest of the surfaces. The occurrence of these 'sticker marks' as they are often called may at times be attributed to the use of dirty, mouldy and wet sticks or sticks of a species with an acid content, such as oak.

In the kiln drying of some species, however, such as iroko, beech and sycamore, even when they are piled with clean dry sticks, well defined stick marks may develop which penetrate so deeply into the material that they are not removed by normal planing. *Plate 9*. This form of staining is due to the chemical changes taking place immediately beneath the sticks, where air is more or less excluded and hence the initial drying is slow, differing from those changes which occur in the fully exposed surface zones. For instance, in iroko it is thought that tannins interact with the calcium salts in this species to a much greater extent under the sticks, where warm moist conditions persist for a considerable time, than elsewhere.

Although very little work has been done on the problem of staining in the region of the piling sticks, it would appear from tests on sycamore that a possible way of avoiding it is to obtain a quick surface drying of the timber before it is piled in stick. This can be done by end-racking the boards or planks, ie by standing them on end against a wall or other support so that the surfaces are freely exposed to the air. This treatment would not be very effective, however, during damp winter months.

3 *Water stain* (notably the familiar dark brown surface stain on oak), is commonly found on timber air seasoned in stacks which have not been adequately protected from rain; it should not occur when timber is kiln dried but occasionally it may be caused by inadvertent wetting of parts of the stack in a kiln. When such trouble develops it can usually be traced to one of the four sources listed at the bottom of the table in section 7.6.

Chapter 4 Air drying

4.0 Introduction

A high proportion of the world's timber is air dried or partly air dried before further drying in a kiln, and this is also true of timber used in the United Kingdom. It is important that this air drying should be carried out as efficiently as possible.

In air drying, the fresh-sawn timber is open-piled out of doors or in open sheds so that the surfaces are exposed to the surrounding atmosphere and evaporation of moisture can commence. Air movement through the stack, caused by winds or local convection currents, can then convey heat to the wood and carry away the vapour coming from it.

As has been stated in 2.2, the rate of air drying depends very largely on the prevailing weather, but to a limited extent both the drying rate and the degrade which occurs can be influenced by the adoption of the correct procedures outlined in the following paragraphs. Some of them do not necessarily apply to countries with climates very different from that of the United Kingdom.

4.1 Drying in the round

Small diameter logs such as those used for fencing posts, telegraph poles, chip or wood wool production, etc, can be air dried in the round. *Plate 10*. To accelerate the drying and reduce the risk of attack from fungi and beetles, the bark should be removed soon after felling and the rounds self-crossed in stacks kept well clear of the ground. In alternate layers there should be fewer poles and these should be spaced apart so that air can move more freely through the stacks. Peeled softwood poles up to about 150 mm (6 in) in diameter will usually dry down to 25 to 30 per cent (a condition suitable for impregnation with preservative) in a matter of 4 to 6 months if put out in the spring, but if stacked in the autumn or winter they will naturally take longer to reach this condition.

Larger logs, especially those of the denser species, will dry very little indeed in the round except in the outermost layers of sapwood and on the ends. It is essential therefore to convert them as soon as possible into boards, planks or dimension stock and to open-pile these immediately after conversion, especially in the warmer months. Staining and insect attack is liable to develop in logs of many species and also in sawn material which is left bulk-piled for more than a few days.

4.2 Site and layout of yard

Ideally, timber should be stacked well away from trees and buildings, on a level, well-drained site from which all vegetation has been cleared and the ground either concreted over, covered with ashes or otherwise treated to prevent renewed growth. When this is not practicable, the site should be cleared in the first instance and all reasonable care taken to keep down the growth of grass and weeds, which tend to interfere with the free circulation of air beneath the stacks. Sawdust and odd pieces of timber should never be left lying on the ground between the stacks since these would quickly rot and harbour insects, and the infection can easily spread to the timber which is being dried.

In most situations, the orientation of the stacks has little effect on the drying rate and the most important consideration in planning the yard is to arrange stacks and roadways to facilitate the necessary handling operations.

Adjacent stacks should be parallel to each other and whether they are to be built with their ends or sides facing the alleys obviously depends on the methods of transport and stacking to be employed. In this respect consideration should be given to any possible future changes such as those occasioned by the acquisition of fork lift trucks or side loaders.

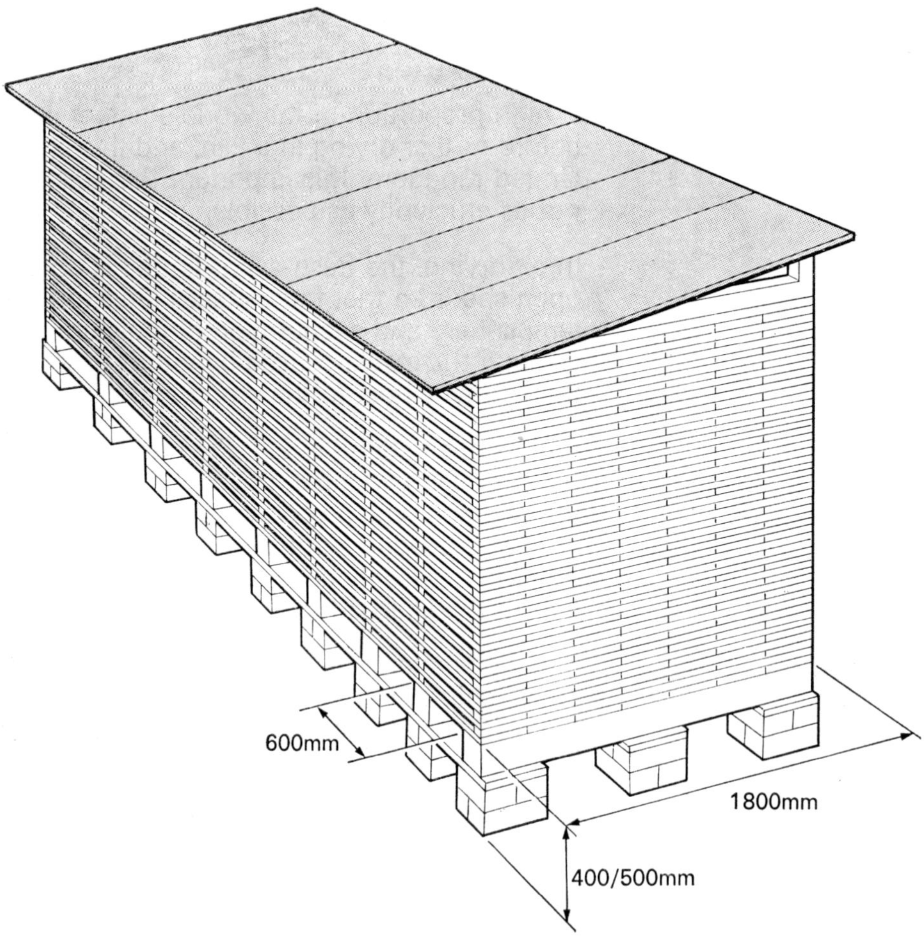

Figure 6 *Recommended stack construction for air seasoning of timber*

4.3 Foundations

Stacks should be erected on good solid foundations and, in order to permit ample ventilation, the bottom layers of timber should be raised well above the ground. *Fig 6*. The clearance should certainly not be less than 230 mm (9 in) and should preferably be about 460 mm (18 in). The most convenient form of foundation, and probably the simplest to erect, consists of a series of timber cross-members not less than 100 × 100 mm (4 × 4 in) in section, preferably creosoted, and lifted clear of the ground on brick or concrete piers or on creosoted timber, eg railway sleepers. The piers should be placed at intervals of 900 mm (3 ft) along the length of each cross-member or bearer, and the bearers themselves should be spaced one behind the other at intervals of 600 mm (2 ft) along the whole length of the stack. Stringers or longitudinal timber members give added strength and rigidity to the foundations, but are seldom indispensable, except in certain circumstances where special stacking arrangements are obviously facilitated by their inclusion. It is essential that the bearers should all be in one plane, but whether level or on a slight slope is of little consequence. In either case, any necessary adjustment can be made by varying the height of the brick piers and inserting wooden packing blocks between the bricks and cross-members where required.

4.4 Stacking the timber

1 Size of stacks

In very wide stacks the timber inside dries slowly, and stain and decay are likely to develop. As a general rule, therefore, a stack should not be wider than 2 m ($6\frac{1}{2}$ ft) and, apart from convenience of handling, there is no advantage in leaving more than about 300 mm (1 ft) between adjacent stacks. The height is limited only by stability and ease of piling. Tall stacks are generally to be preferred, however, especially in the case of hardwoods such as beech and elm which have a natural tendency to distort.

2 Piling sticks

Except in the special cases of certain classes of dimension stock, piling sticks should always be used to separate the layers of timber. The planks or boards themselves should not be used as separators, since practically no drying will take place at the areas of contact and stain or decay is likely to develop at these places. Whenever possible the sticks should be of clean, dry timber; the sizes most generally required are 25 × 25 mm (1 × 1 in) and 25 × 13 mm (1 × $\frac{1}{2}$ in). It is by varying the thickness of piling sticks that some control of the drying rate can be achieved. Softwoods, which will tolerate a fairly fast drying rate without degrade, can be piled with 25 mm (1 in) sticks at all times of the year, and there is some advantage in using even thicker sticks, say 38 mm ($1\frac{1}{2}$ in), if they are piled during the winter. On the other hand, some hardwoods, notably oak and beech, are very liable to split if the surface of the wood is dried too rapidly and, whereas it is safe to use 25 mm (1 in) sticks when piling these timbers in winter, it is advisable not to use sticks thicker than 13 mm ($\frac{1}{2}$ in) in spring and summer.

It should be realised that besides separating the layers of timber to allow a free circulation of air, piling sticks when correctly placed also to some extent restrain the timber from warping during drying. Ideally, therefore, the spacing between the piling sticks should be varied according to the species and thickness of the timber which is to be dried. Since it is obviously impracticable to vary the spacing and position of the bearers for every thickness and species likely to be handled on one site, it will probably be found convenient to deal with the timber in the following manner. Softwoods (except larch) and those hardwoods which show little tendency to warp, when sawn to thicknesses of 50 mm (2 in) and upwards, should be piled with the

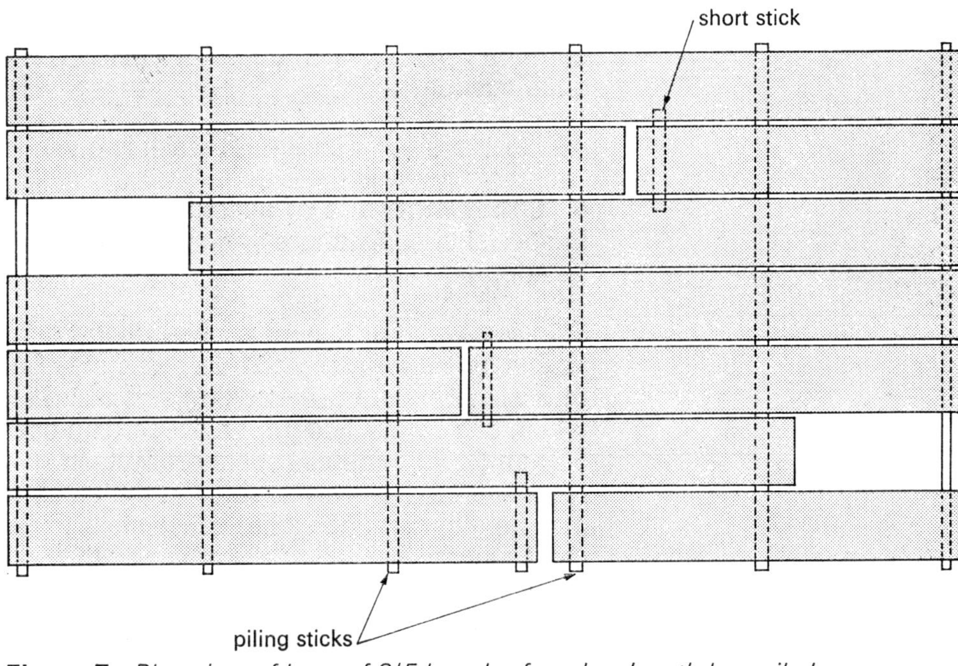

Figure 7 *Plan view of layer of S/E boards of random length box-piled*

vertical rows of sticks spaced at intervals of 1200 mm (4 ft), but for thinner boards it is advisable to reduce the space to 600 mm (2 ft). Larch and hardwoods such as beech, birch and elm, which tend to distort considerably during drying, should have sticks at 600 mm (2 ft) intervals even when sawn to thicknesses of 50 mm (2 in), and the same spacing could, for convenience, be used without undue risk with boards down to 25 mm (1 in) in thickness. Boards of these species, more particularly elm, less than 25 mm (1 in) in thickness, are best stacked with the sticks spaced only about 300 mm (12 in) apart. With such close spacing as this it is advisable to incorporate longitudinal stringers in the foundations, so as to obviate the need for introducing an unduly large number of cross-members.

3 Normal stacking procedure

Whenever possible, different species and thicknesses should be stacked separately. It is an advantage if the planks or boards can be sorted to length at the outset, and when a variety of lengths has to be stacked it is convenient to place the longest planks at the bottom and to reduce the length of the stack as the height increases. Alternatively, if sorting beforehand is not practicable, a stack of uniform length may be built by arranging the boards as shown in Figure 7. This is sometimes referred to as box-piling.

Sticks should be laid on the cross-bearers before the bottom layer of timber is put on, and it should be arranged for a vertical line of sticks to be built as near to the ends of the boards as possible. To do this, it may in some cases be necessary to make slight adjustments to the spacing of the foundations at the ends of the stacks. As piling proceeds, care should be taken to place the sticks in each line vertically one above the other, so that the weight of the stack is directly transmitted from each stick to the one below. Distortional degrade may be considerably reduced by a proper arrangement of the piling sticks, but mis-alignment tends to aggravate such defects.

The ends of boards, especially if they are thin, are liable to distort badly if unsupported, and when it is impossible to avoid introducing a number of long boards which overhang the ends of the stack, special supports for these should be erected. Within the stack itself short lengths of stick should be inserted under the ends of boards which do not reach the vertical lines of piling sticks. It is not advisable to place boards close together, since this restricts the free movement of air within a stack and may cause stain or decay to develop on the edges. A space of about 25 mm (1 in) between adjacent boards will generally be found to be quite adequate.

An illustration of a well built stack is given in Figure 6.

4 Other methods of stacking

In special circumstances various non-standard methods of stacking may be adopted.

Self-crossing. For instance when drying dimension stock of convenient sizes such as squares and rails these may be open piled by self-crossing, thus obviating the use of piling sticks and increasing the quantity which can be stacked per unit area. The use of pieces much above 50 mm (2 in) wide as separators instead of sticks is not to be recommended, however, since in the areas covered by them drying may be retarded enough to cause stain to develop. Furthermore, the cross pieces themselves distorting as they dry will exert less restraint on the layers of timber they are separating.

Piling of boules. It is often economic and desirable to leave boards or planks unedged until they are air dried and ready for further conversion into shaped pieces, such as curved chair-legs. Advantage can then be taken of any natural curves in the trunk from which they were sawn. There is also a demand for boards or planks all cut from the same log so that by taking adjacent pieces they can be readily matched for figure and colour.

In both these cases the unedged pieces may be piled in log form as illustrated in Plate 11. Use of this method reduces handling to a minimum since the planks can be piled straight off the saw and each boule pile transported as a unit. Further measurement is avoided in cases where logs are bought and sold on Hoppus measure.

The drying of timber in log form tends to be faster than in normal stacks because each pile is narrow and has plenty of space round it. It is customary therefore to use sticks only 13 or 19 mm ($\frac{1}{2}$ or $\frac{3}{4}$ in) thick when log piling, in spring or summer, species which are prone to surface check.

End-racking. In the drying of certain species, such as sycamore, special precautions must be taken if the light colour is to be preserved and stain and stick marks are to be avoided. It is beneficial to dry off the surfaces as rapidly as possible, and a simple way of doing this is to pile the sawn pieces vertically against a wall or some form of rack which keeps them at least 25 mm (1 in) apart.

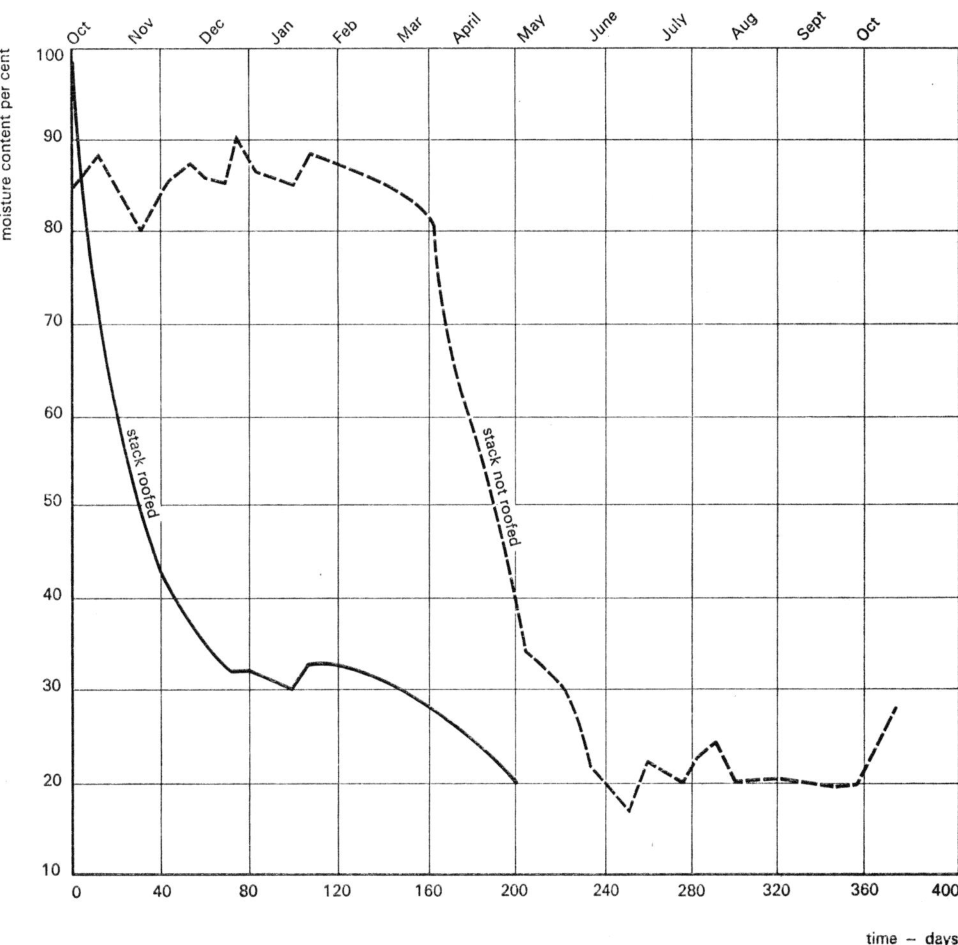

Figure 8 *Effect of roofing on rate of drying 100 × 50 mm Sitka spruce in W. Scotland*

4.5 Roofs

Ideally, timber for air drying should be stacked in large, open-sided sheds but when these are not available some form of roof should be provided to protect the timber in every stack from heavy rain and from the full heat of the sun. It has been shown that, in a well covered stack, drying proceeds quite well in winter even in a high rainfall area whereas little or no drying occurs in a stack exposed to the weather. *Fig 8*.

A weatherboard roof with a good fall to one side and large enough to overhang the stack by a generous amount is ideal and it can be used repeatedly. Roofs can also be constructed of corrugated metal or of frames covered with heavy gauge polythene sheet. All roofs need to be firmly secured and a simple method of doing this is depicted in Figure 9.

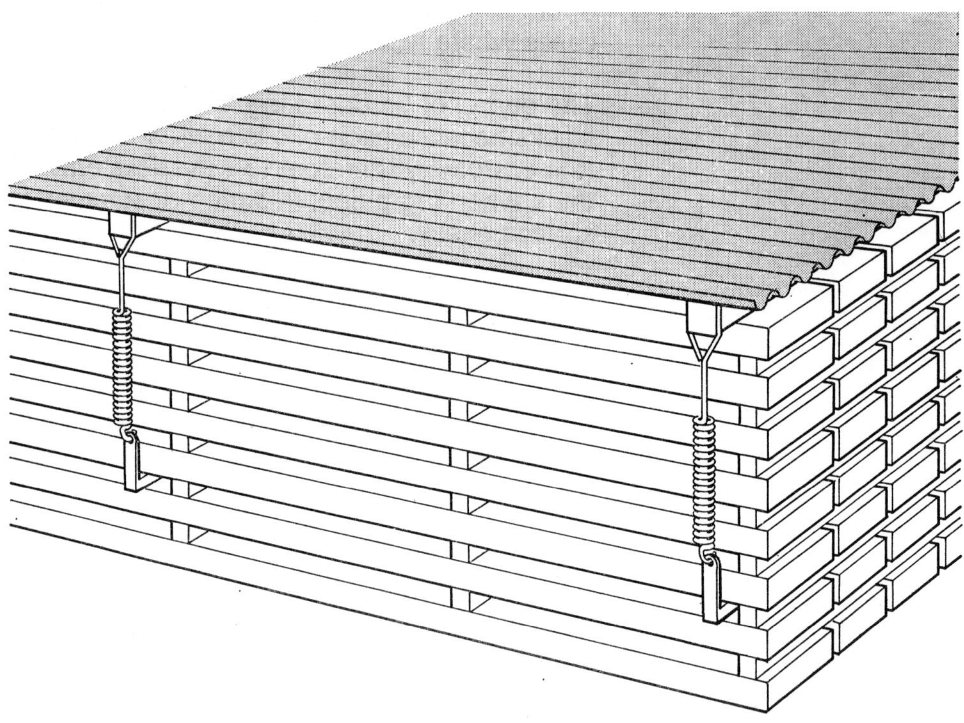

Figure 9 *Method of securing roofs on air drying stacks*

Should it be found impracticable to make and handle proper roofs some useful cover and protection from the sun can be obtained by placing rough slabs or boards on top of the stacks. A sheet of polythene spread over the stack and held in position by the last layer of timber is better than nothing, as it ensures that the rain runs down the outside and not downwards into all parts of the stack.

4.6 Protection for the ends of the timber

One of the commonest forms of degrade which occurs during air seasoning is checking or splitting at the ends of boards and planks. This may reach serious proportions when green timber, especially certain hardwoods, such as oak and beech, is put out to dry in hot summer weather. The damage is caused by the exposed ends drying out more rapidly and tending to shrink to a greater degree than the bulk of timber. The tendency for this to happen may be considerably reduced by protecting the ends from the sun and air. The best method of doing this is to apply to the ends a good moisture-proof coating such as bituminous paint or a wax emulsion, and on large material this coating may conveniently be brushed on to the timber after it has been stacked.

When end coating is ruled out on account of the expense or labour involved, it may be feasible at least to shade the exposed ends of boards by draping tarpaulins or sacking over the ends of the stack. Wooden cleats fixed to the ends of the boards give some protection, but if these are used they should either be nailed in the middle only or should be very thin, so that they buckle as the boards shrink. Strong, securely nailed cleats tend to restrain the natural shrinkage, and may actually induce splitting or cause initial splits to extend.

4.7 Time to stack the timber

Timber is commonly converted and stacked at all times of the year, and provided stacking follows conversion with the minimum of delay and is properly carried out, serious damage need not occur simply because the work has not been done at the most suitable season. When a choice of seasons exists, however, there can be no doubt that it is best to stack hardwoods in the winter months when the drying conditions are mild, and softwoods in the spring when comparatively rapid drying conditions may be anticipated. This is because many hardwoods are liable to split if dried too rapidly during the early stages, whereas softwoods are tolerant of more severe conditions and are less likely to be affected by sap-stain if the surface of the timber is dried off quickly.

It should be realised that although in very dry summer weather the moisture content of air dried stock may fall to about 15 per cent, the average for timber dried entirely in the open in this country is nearer 20 per cent. Once this value has been reached, therefore, from the seasoning point of view, there is little, if any, advantage to be gained by further exposing the timber to the elements.

4.8 Gauging the progress of drying

It is desirable to have some knowledge of how the air drying of timber is proceeding so that the timber need not be left in the stacks once it is down to the required moisture content or to the lowest moisture content it is likely to attain under outdoor conditions.

Ideally, a few sample boards should be incorporated in the stack so that they can be withdrawn and weighed at any time. If initially prepared in the same way as are the kiln samples described in section 9.2.1 their moisture content can be estimated. More practically, tests with a moisture meter should suffice to give an approximate idea of the dryness of the timber if it is below about 30 per cent. The long insulated pin electrodes referred to in 1.4.3 should be used and it must be remembered that readings taken only on pieces on the edge or protruding beyond the ends of stacks will not always give a true indication of the moisture content of the bulk of the pile.

4.9 Drying times

It is impossible to give other than very approximate average times taken to air dry various timber items, for obviously these times vary markedly with the weather over any particular period. The following times are given as a rough guide to assist in planning air seasoning operations.

Softwoods 25 mm (1 in) thick, if piled in spring, should dry to about 20 per cent moisture content in 1½ to 3 months; 50 mm (2 in) thick softwoods will require 3 to 4 months under similar conditions. Hardwoods 25 mm thick, if piled in the autumn should dry to about 20 per cent by the following summer, whereas under favourable conditions 50 mm hardwoods should dry in a year if piled in October or November.

4.10 Cost of air drying

The cost of air drying, excluding that of handling, depends on a number of factors. These are:

1 the capital cost of establishing the drying yard, including preparation of the site, provision of roads, foundations, piling sticks and roofs.

2 value of the land.

3 value of the timber and current rate of interest on capital.

4 overheads including depreciation, maintenance, supervision, insurance, etc.

5 the time taken to dry, a very variable and unpredictable factor depending as it does on the particular weather conditions encountered as well as on the species and thickness of the timber.

The major component in the cost of air drying is usually the interest on the value of the timber held in stock.

The cost per unit volume is directly proportional to the time taken. It follows that when air drying is being carried out prior to kilning it may be economic to transfer the timber to the kiln when at 30 to 35 per cent, rather than wait the disproportionately long time often needed to complete the air drying to around 20 per cent.

The provision of good drying facilities, including roofs, accounts for only a small part of the total cost, especially when valuable timber has to be dried. There is little doubt that the provision of stack covers pays for itself in a relatively short time.

Chapter 5
Timber drying kilns

5.0 Introduction

A timber drying kiln may be defined simply as a 'closed structure designed or adapted for the purpose of reducing the moisture content of timber or timber-based products'.

It follows from the general principles of kiln drying outlined in 2.1 that an efficient kiln must provide four essential features, viz heating, ventilation, humidification and air circulation. *Plate 12.*

Heating is needed to keep the air at any temperature between 35°C and 100°C and this is usually effected by steam pipes (plain or gilled) in coils or radiators. Steam may be raised in boilers using wood waste as fuel if large, unmarketable quantities are available but automatic, oil-fired boilers may often prove a better proposition, being both labour-saving and independent of the vagaries of a wood fuel supply.

Electricity and gas are seldom used for heating in timber dryers. In small plants where the installation of a steam boiler would form a large part of the overall cost oil-fired air heaters can be an economic alternative to steam. *Plate 13.* Another form of heating occasionally adopted consists of circulating a heated mineral oil at atmospheric pressure through heating coils as in a hot water system.

Ventilation of the kiln chamber by air interchange through adjustable openings in the structure must be provided in order to keep the relative humidity down to the required levels when large quantities of moisture are being rapidly evaporated from the timber. Dehumidifiers are sometimes used as an alternative means of ridding kilns of surplus moisture (see 2.3.5).

Humidification is sometimes needed to keep the humidity at the desired level when the moisture coming from the wood is insufficient to do this. It is particularly needed towards the end of a drying run and is essential for applying final high humidity treatments (see Chapters 9 and 10). Humidification is simply achieved by admitting live steam when this is available but in its absence either water atomisers or a simple, electrically heated, low pressure steam evaporator may be used.

Air circulation is required to convey heat to and moisture away from all parts of the kiln load. It is the aim in modern kiln design to promote a strong uniform flow of air through the stack at closely controlled temperature and humidity conditions. It is in the way in which, and the degree to which, this is achieved that the various types of kiln mainly differ.

5.1 Progressive and compartment kilns

Drying kilns can be divided into two broad categories—progressive (continuous process) and compartment (batch process).

In the progressive kiln, the timber loaded on bogies is moved at intervals through a long chamber during drying and is subjected to hotter and drier air conditions as it progresses towards the exit.

In a compartment kiln the timber remains stationary and the temperature and humidity of the circulated air are altered in accordance with a schedule designed to suit the material being dried (see 9.3).

A large progressive kiln is cheaper to install and operate than a battery of compartment kilns giving the same total output. However, approximately uniform final moisture contents can only be obtained when a continuous supply of timber with closely similar drying characteristics and not varying too widely in initial moisture contents is available. Since these conditions very seldom occur in the UK, few progressive kilns have been installed and it is therefore not proposed to deal further with them. It can be said that if properly designed and used (with forced circulation) they provide a means of automatically exposing timber during successive stages of drying to conditions which may follow closely those required for good seasoning.

Compartment kilns, on the other hand, are more accommodating in that a wide variety of loads can be accepted and each given an appropriate drying treatment. A battery of medium sized kilns (each of about 15 to 25 m^3 capacity) is often better than two or three large units in that it gives the flexibility in planning of throughput which is very desirable in firms which have to dry a diversity of species and thicknesses for various end-uses.

It may also be advantageous in large plants to have two or three different lengths of kiln so that with consignments of timber of varying length it is easier to make up loads to fill every kiln from end to end.

5.2 Compartment kilns

Practically all compartment kilns are now of the forced draught internal fan type.

1 Developments in kiln design

In the earliest kilns the timber was open stacked over a basement containing some form of heating, for example steam pipes or flue pipes from a wood burning furnace. The only movement of air was that caused by the hot air producing a natural upward draught augmented by the chimney effect of vents in the roof. Inevitably the air circulation was very slow and irregular and speeds seldom exceeded about 0·15 m/s ($\frac{1}{2}$ ft/s) through the stack.

These natural draught kilns were followed by various designs of forced draught kilns in many of which air, heated and humidified outside the drying chamber, was delivered through a system of ducting into one side, passed through the timber pile, and then was pulled back into an external fan, nearly always of the centrifugal type. In these kilns an average air speed of up to about 0·5 m/s ($1\frac{1}{2}$ ft/s) was obtainable but difficulty was encountered in achieving satisfactory longitudinal uniformity in units of commercial length. Also, without an additional system of ducting, reversal of the air flow was not possible.

It was found that an adequate and sufficiently uniform distribution of air through the whole load could best be obtained by situating fans within the kiln itself and in nearly all of these the internal fans are of the propeller type.

Modern internal fan kilns may conveniently be classified as belonging to the overhead fan type and the side fan type and the commonest designs of these are described briefly in the sections below.

The air speed requirements of a kiln and hence the size, speed and arrangement of fans should be dictated by the type of drying to be carried out. For most hardwoods and for all timber previously partly air dried the air speed through the timber stacks should average between 1·0 and 1·5 metres per second (3 and 5 ft/s). For free-drying light hardwoods and softwoods it should average about 1·8 to 2·1 m/s (6 to 7 ft/s) and up to 2·4 m/s (8 ft/s) or more when the air has a long path to travel through the timber stack before it is re-heated.

Except in kilns with very high air speeds or in those holding only narrow stacks of timber, means of reversing the air flow at regular intervals should be provided. Maximum drying rates on both sides of the stack and greater uniformity across it can be achieved by automatic, frequent reversal of circulation.

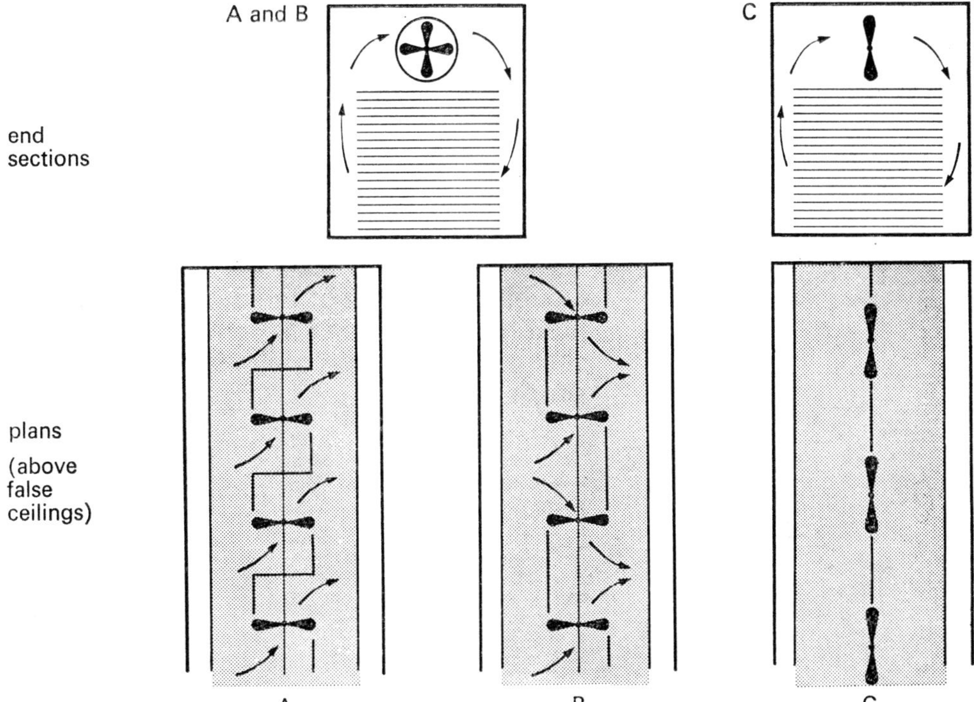

Figure 10 *Fan arrangement in three designs of overhead fan kiln*

2 Overhead fan kilns

1 Longitudinal shaft design

In two of the designs of overhead fan kilns the fans are mounted at regular intervals on a longitudinal shaft. The air is diverted to flow across the top of the kiln above a false ceiling and down into the side duct and through the stack by baffle boxes as in the designs shown in Figure 10A and B (both sometimes called cross circulation kilns).

In design A, in spite of correcting plate baffles fixed as indicated, there is a tendency for the circulation to be stronger at the end towards which the fans are blowing.

The longitudinal drift is eliminated in design B in which left hand and right hand fans are fitted alternately on the shaft. Some slight loss in efficiency of fans occurs due to the pairs opposing each other setting up back pressure.

In these longitudinal shaft kilns, air speeds through the stack average only from 0·5 to 1 m/s ($1\frac{1}{2}$ to 3 ft/s) unless fans larger than the usual 0·8 to 1·0 m ($2\frac{1}{2}$ to 3 ft) diameter are used. In America kilns are built to design B using fans up to 1·8 m (6 ft) in diameter.

2 Cross shaft design of overhead fan kiln

In the cross shaft overhead fan kiln, one of the two most commonly used designs in the UK, the fans are mounted on short shafts aligned across the kiln as depicted in Figure 10C. Hence the air is delivered primarily in the required direction and, apart from the vertical bulkhead embracing the fans and stopping short circuiting, no deflecting boxes and baffles are required. *Plate 12*. Alignment and maintenance of long shafts are avoided but on the other hand, when cross shaft kilns are built side by side in large batteries, the problem arises of how best to drive the fans. This is met by the various kiln manufacturers in a number of ways, including (a) the use of internal motors insulated to withstand kiln conditions (b) chain drives in tubes passing through the roof of the kiln and (c) mounting fans at an angle and driving them through inclined shafts passing out through the roof to belt drives and motor/s above, which are also mounted at an angle.

The fans used in cross shaft kilns range in diameter from 0·8 to 1·8 m ($2\frac{1}{2}$ to 6 ft) and average air speeds through the stack vary from about 0·9 to 1·8 m/s (3 to 6 ft/s) with satisfactory uniformity along the length.

Plate 12 illustrates a typical cross shaft overhead fan kiln and shows the relative positions of fans, heating pipes, steam spray and vents.

Double stack units of the overhead cross shaft kiln can be built, left and right hand fans being fitted above each stack on a common shaft. The cost per unit volume of timber held is somewhat less than for two single units.

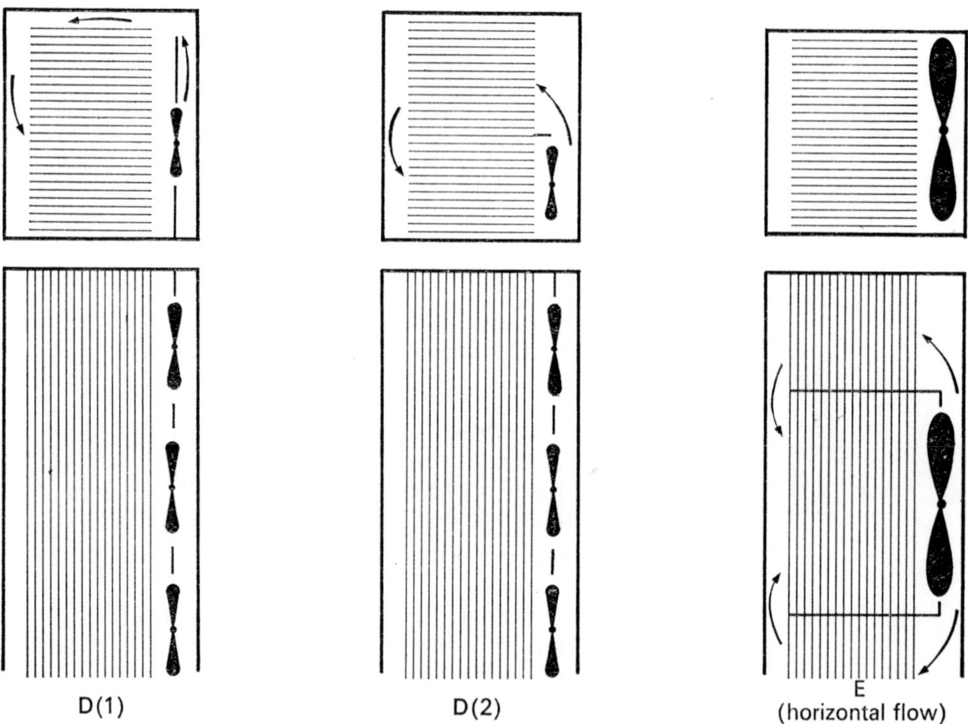

Figure 11 *Fan arrangement in three designs of side fan kiln*

3 Side fan kilns

There are two distinctive designs of kiln shown in Figure 11D and E in which large propeller type fans are placed to one side of the timber load (or between the two stacks in a variation called a double stack unit). In both of these, large slow-running fans can be used without necessitating the increased height of building involved in using them in overhead fan kilns—and advantage can readily be taken of the fact that the larger the fan the more efficient it is in terms of volume of air moved per unit of power consumed.

In design D(1) the air is delivered or returned through a duct above the timber load and no transverse baffles are required. In a variation of this design occasionally adopted and shown in diagram D(2), smaller fans are mounted to one side of the lower half of the timber pile and the air returns not through a duct but through the upper half of the pile as indicated.

In design E, which is the type commonly installed in the UK and in some European countries in recent years, the air flow is unique in that it is horizontal throughout. As is indicated in the diagram, this is brought about by filling the kiln to its full height and with the wing baffles forming a fan box, air is pushed or pulled (according to the direction of fan rotation) through the portion of the stack opposite the fan and pulled or pushed through the two end portions.

It is evident that in this design the air has to pass through the stack twice before it is reheated (unless booster heating pipes are placed in the duct remote from the fans) and hence fast air speeds are necessary to minimize the lag in drying rate across the width. Average speeds of the order of 1·5 to 2·4 m/s (5 to 8 ft/s) are obtained without excessive power consumption by the use of large fans (1·5 to 2·4 m in diameter). The air speeds through various parts of a timber load are not usually as uniform as in the overhead cross shaft type of kiln but the lowest speed anywhere is sufficient for satisfactory drying. The frequent reversal in direction of air flow now practised in most kilns tends to compensate for local variations in speed as well as fulfilling its main function of shortening drying times by reducing lag in drying rate across the width.

An interior view of a side fan kiln is given in Plate 14 and a large battery of prefabricated metal units of this type is shown in Plate 15.

Side fan kilns can also be built as double stack units, the one large fan pulling air through the stack on one side of it and pushing the air through that on the other.

4 Comparison between overhead cross shaft and side fan kilns

The advantages of the horizontal flow side fan type compared with the overhead cross shaft type may be summarised as follows:

1 Large fan is accommodated in a moderate height of kiln.

2 High average air flow is attained at reasonable power cost.

3 Air flow is not affected much by irregularities in pile face (see 9.1.1).

4 Fan/s and pipes etc are supported from ground so kiln shell requires less strength.

5 Fans and pipes are more easily accessible for maintenance.

On the other hand in side fan units:

1 The length of air travel through the timber stack is greater.

2 The variation in air speed through the stack from one part to another is greater.

3 The air flow is not satisfactory near the ends of loads which are appreciably shorter than the kiln.

4 The kiln takes up more width for equivalent capacity.

5 Construction of kiln shell

Until the late 1940's nearly all timber drying kilns were of brick and/or concrete construction. Prefabricated all-metal units were then introduced and, although at first more costly, the number installed steadily increased. Currently there are more metal units being installed than brick ones and they have become competitive in price.

Most overhead fan kilns are brick built as the shell has to support the fans, heating pipes etc. The side fan kilns are more often than not made of prefabricated, insulated aluminium panels. When the aluminium sheets used are of high purity metal they withstand kiln conditions with the minimum of maintenance. Good design and workmanship in manufacture are essential in order to achieve satisfactory and lasting levels of heat insulation in the metal panels.

The metal units, being relatively light in weight, do not need such deep and hence expensive foundations as brick kilns, an important point if the only site available is on made-up land. They can be erected quickly and if necessary in the replanning or moving of works they can be dismantled for installation elsewhere, as can other production machines.

When plant is used for short drying runs on timbers which tolerate high temperatures, metal kilns are more durable and have the advantage over those of brick and concrete construction in that they can be warmed up more rapidly.

6 Size of plant

When installing new kilns which are to be used for specific purposes and species, the probable drying times need to be known before the capacity required can be estimated. A general guide to these times is given in Appendix B.

Particular care should be taken in deciding on the optimum length, as well as the capacity of the kilns, so that they will be filled from end to end and top to bottom as often as possible.

Chapter 6
Kiln instrumentation

6.1 Ancillary equipment

Apart from the instruments required on the kilns themselves, an operator needs very little equipment in order to carry out his duties efficiently. The balance and drying oven for moisture content determination and the electrical moisture meter for quick tests on other than green timber have been described in sections 1.4.2 and 1.4.3.

It is essential to have a pair of scales and set of weights for the weighing of kiln samples (see 9.2.3). The scales should be of a fairly robust type and capable of weighing up to 50 kg (or 100 lb) with an accuracy of ±10 gm (or ±0·02 lb). The accuracy should be checked from time to time and zero adjustment made when necessary.

In the running of a large battery, where a large number of samples has to be weighed daily, time can be saved by using more expensive scales of the semi-automatic type. *Plate 16*. Other time saving equipment includes:

1 a conveniently situated power driven band saw to be used for cutting samples, for moisture testing, preparation of the kiln samples and casehardening tests.

2 a slide-rule or other calculator for quick moisture content calculations.

6.2 Kiln hygrometers

It is obviously essential for an operator to have some means of determining the temperature and humidity of the circulating air as it enters the pile of timber. A simple, cheap and yet efficient instrument for this purpose is the wet- and dry-bulb hygrometer consisting of two mercury- or spirit-in-glass thermometers. The bulb of one of these is kept wet by a fabric sleeve and wick (or a continuous tubular wick fitted on to it) which conducts water up from a reservoir supported underneath it as shown in Figure 12.

The evaporation of moisture from the wet fabric cools it and the thermometer bulb to a temperature below that of the dry-bulb. The lower the humidity of the air the faster the rate of evaporation and the greater the depression of the wet-bulb temperature.

A definite relationship exists between dry-bulb temperature, depression of the wet-bulb temperature and relative humidity so that tables such as those provided in Appendix F can be drawn up, from which it is possible to determine the third value, given any two. The following examples illustrate the manner in which these tables can be used.

If the dry-bulb thermometer of a hygrometer in a kiln reads 140°F and the wet-bulb 123°F, giving a depression of 17°F, it is seen that the relative humidity must be 60 per cent.

Taking a case when it is required to operate a kiln at 70°C and a relative humidity of 75 per cent it is seen from Table F2 that the wet-bulb depression must be 6°C so the wet-bulb must be controlled to a temperature of 64°C with the dry-bulb at 70°C.

A further factor influencing the wet-bulb depression at the various humidities is the air speed over the wet fabric, there being a 'boundary layer' effect as in the drying of wet wood. However, the temperature and air speeds prevailing in drying kilns are such that no significant errors are incurred by using Tables F2 and F3 which are based on air speeds over the bulbs of 1 to 1·5 m/s.

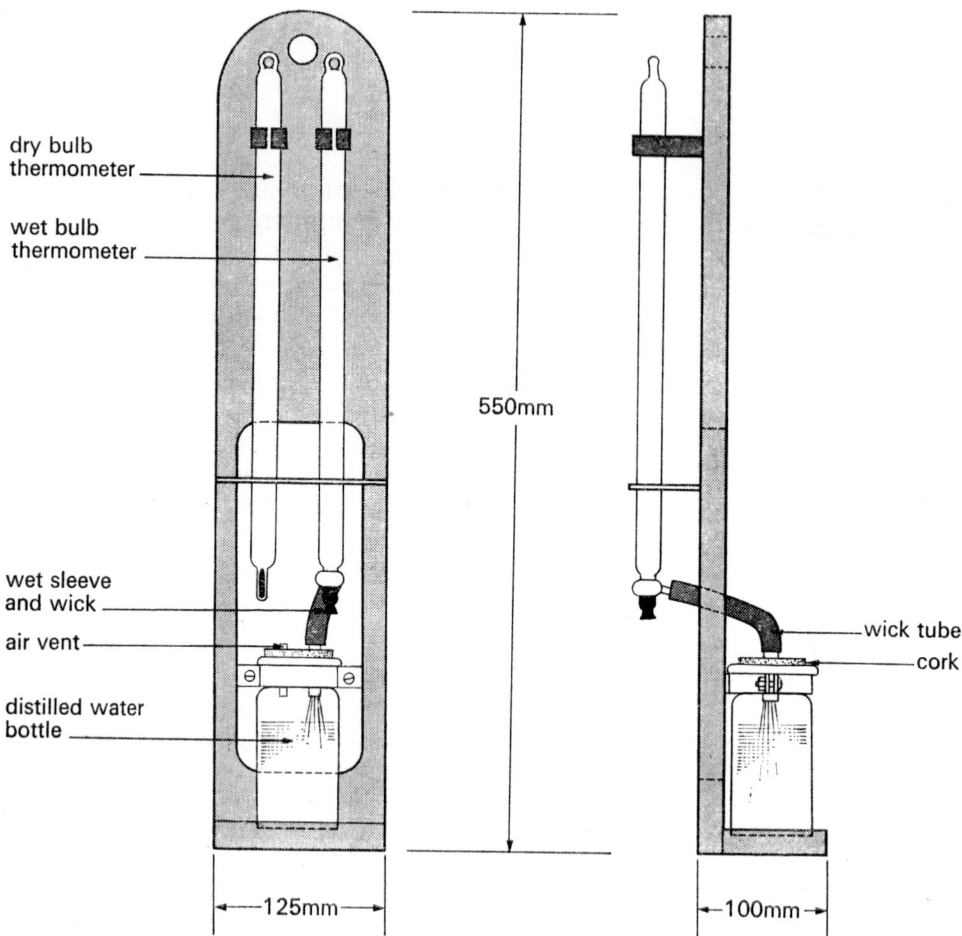

Figure 12 *Wet- and dry-bulb hygrometer*

In order that hygrometers may be read with reasonable accuracy from outside the kiln, the thermometer used should be of a type which has a wide stem and a clearly defined graduated scale which is easily read with the naked eye from some 1200 to 1500 mm (4 to 5 ft) away, or further away with the aid of low power binoculars or opera glasses.

A suitable type of mercury-in-glass insulated thermometer generally supplied for use in kilns has a white opaque scale graduated from 10° to 100°C in 1°C divisions. Fahrenheit thermometers may be used but experience has shown that the more open centigrade scale is generally easier to read. Occasionally an operator may wish to convert from one temperature scale to another: for example, when he has centigrade thermometers and the schedule he has to follow is given only in degrees Fahrenheit. For such contingencies the conversion chart for the two temperature scales given in Appendix F will be found useful.

It should be mentioned here that hair or paper element type hygrometers are not generally suitable for use in kilns since their reactions to humidity are affected when exposed to high temperatures.

1 Calibration

The types of thermometers suitable for kiln use are liable to give readings differing from the true temperature by as much as 1°C and occasionally even more. The effect on the timber of running a kiln

1 or 2 degrees high or low in temperature is not significant but it will be appreciated that when using wet- and dry-bulb thermometers to determine humidity any inaccuracy may lead to a serious error in calculating the humidity. For instance, if a kiln is set to run at 45°C and 80 per cent relative humidity and the dry-bulb reads 1·5°C lower and the wet-bulb 0·5°C higher than the true temperatures, the net result of these errors will be that the kiln is actually at 46·5°C and a relative humidity of only 70 per cent (see humidity Table F2). A kiln humidity 10 per cent lower than that required in a schedule may well cause splitting in any green, refractory hardwood. Ideally, each thermometer should be calibrated against a standard thermometer and the corrections so obtained applied to the readings taken in a kiln. Calibration certificates can usually be purchased with thermometers but an operator can fairly simply carry out the calibration himself.

For this calibration it is not essential to have an actual 'standard thermometer' accurate to very fine limits but it is as well to have a good quality mercury-in-glass thin stem thermometer with a scale of 10°C to 100°C etched on the stem in 1°C divisions. This should be carefully kept aside for the calibration of kiln thermometers and recorders, in which the following procedure should be adopted:

Immerse the thin stem thermometer in a vessel of water with four or six of the kiln thermometers, numbered or lettered for identification, clustered closely round it. Warm the water to about 40°C, and hold the temperature at this value for a couple of minutes or so, stirring constantly to keep the water at a uniform temperature throughout. Then take readings of all the thermometers. This process should be repeated at roughly 20°C intervals up to 100°C.

When a thermometer reads 1°C below the standard at 60°C, for example, it is said to have a correction of +1°C at that temperature. Using this thermometer in controlling a kiln to 60°C the operator, by applying the correction figure of +1°C, will know that when the reading obtained is 59°C the actual temperature is the required one of 60°C.

A simpler method of allowing for thermometer errors and one quite generally adopted where a fairly large number of thermometers are available is that of making up hygrometers of pairs of thermometers which read within ½°C of each other when kept in water at 60°C. The error in relative humidity involved when using such hygrometers will then seldom exceed 2 or 3 per cent.

2 Position of hygrometer in the kiln

In all kilns in which the air circulation is reversed at infrequent intervals there should be a hygrometer on each side of the stack so that whichever way the air is moving its condition as it enters the stack may be determined. Each hygrometer should be placed in the main air flow with neither of the bulbs nearer than 150 mm (6 in) to the adjacent wall. The instrument should be not less than 1200 mm (4 ft) from an end port so that in the time taken to read the two temperatures they will be little affected by the port being opened. The dry-bulb temperature should be read first as it tends to change more rapidly than the wet.

One simple method of fixing a hygrometer in position in a kiln is to attach a short stick, slightly thinner than the piling sticks used for the load, at right angles to the top of the hygrometer frame and after the loading is completed, to insert this stick into any suitably situated gap between two layers of timber.

Alternatively, permanent brackets for the hygrometer may be fixed to the side walls or on stands in central ducts, but in either case it is advisable to remove and store hygrometers in a special rack when the kilns in which they are used are being loaded or unloaded.

In order to obtain accurate readings of kiln hygrometers without difficulty, it is essential that they should be well illuminated. Steam-tight bulkhead lights inside the kilns are very effective, but special, non-corrodable, steam-tight conduit and fittings must be used. Lights outside the kiln directed through glass windows and focused on the hygrometer provide a satisfactory alternative.

When the hygrometers are being placed in position prior to starting up a kiln, the operator should adjust each individual thermometer by rotating it very slowly until the clearest reading of the mercury is obtained. It may be found necessary to tilt the hygrometers slightly from the vertical in order to avoid sheen on the glass stems or deceptive shadows which might lead to false readings.

3 Maintenance

The thermometers should be inspected occasionally to make sure that none has a divided mercury or spirit thread. Apart from this and checking the calibration about once a year, the care of a hygrometer is confined to maintaining the wet-bulb covering in good condition. The water in the reservoir must, of course, be kept at an adequate level.

It is of great importance that the wet-bulb sleeve and wick should be wet and clean, allowing free evaporation from the sleeve and efficient syphoning from the reservoir, and for this reason, particularly in hard water districts, distilled water should be used. Condensate collected from kiln heating-coil returns is usually found satisfactory and really clean rain water may also be used. The sleeve and wick will need changing periodically, usually at least every month, and more frequently when the kiln is being run at a high temperature or when a timber such as oak is being dried and the acid extracts from it adversely affect the cotton or wool fabric.

Ordinary surgical bandage can be used for the wet-bulb covering, in which case only two or three turns should be applied and tied neatly at top and bottom, any loose ends being cut off, since they use up water unnecessarily and tend to cause local drying of the covering. The fitting of the bandage will be made easier if it is first wetted.

The wick may very conveniently be made of 5 or 6 strands of hygrometer cotton string looped and pulled just tightly enough to hold it firmly at the top of the sleeve.

An alternative to the fabric covering and wick is the tubular wick now obtainable. This is slipped over the thermometer bulb and leads directly to the water reservoir. The dry wick can quickly be introduced into the glass tube (which is to prevent evaporation when the wick is syphoning up water) simply by sucking it through. Before the hygrometer is put into use, the sleeve and wick should be soaked with water. Care should be taken to ensure that the hands are free from oil or grease when changing hygrometer wicks.

If a wet-bulb covering dries up completely it soon becomes obvious because the wet-bulb reading rises to that of the dry-bulb. What can be far more serious and rather more difficult to detect is the partial drying of the covering which sometimes occurs. In such an event, shutting down the steam spray in an attempt to lower the wet-bulb reading will cause the kiln humidity to fall still further below the desired value. Partial drying of the wet-bulb should be suspected if its temperature rises whilst other wet bulbs remain steady, and if, for no apparent reason, the spray valve has to be shut down appreciably in order to bring the wet-bulb of the control hygrometer down to the reading required.

Whilst it is of the utmost importance that the covering of hygrometer and recorder wet-bulbs should be kept wet, it is equally essential that the dry-bulbs should be kept quite dry. Difficulty is seldom experienced, but occasionally the bulbs may get placed where the drips from a steam spray or from condensation on the underside of a poorly insulated roof can cause wetting of the dry-bulb, resulting in erratic and falsely low readings. If the cause cannot readily be eliminated, then as a temporary measure a small rubber sheet umbrella may be fitted above the bulb of a thermometer or a small metal shield placed above a recorder dry-bulb but not so near to it as to eliminate all air movement over it.

6.3 Wet- and dry-bulb temperature recorders

In the older kilns, in which there is no automatic control equipment, there is usually at least an instrument which gives a continuous record on a chart outside the kiln of the wet- and dry-bulb temperatures within. These recorders are easy to read, they provide a record from which the kiln conditions applied throughout any particular run may be checked, and are a practical aid in the actual operation of a kiln when this is by hand control. For instance, the operator can see at a glance which way the temperatures are changing and, on making an adjustment in valve setting, can tell readily what effect this is having without taking several readings of a hygrometer. In the case of kilns left unattended during the night, recorders are particularly useful as they will tell the operator on duty next morning how the kilns have been behaving.

Operators should be aware of the limitations of temperature recorders. In some of them there is a lag in their response to changes in temperature owing to the relatively large mass of their bulbs. The chief drawback to recording instruments, however, is that errors in the temperatures indicated, which are not easy to detect, are liable to develop owing to such causes as rough handling of the pen arms when changing the charts. Recorders, therefore, have to be checked for calibration fairly frequently, whereas the simple mercury-in-glass thermometer is more sensitive and precise, and is either functioning perfectly or is quite obviously broken and in need of replacement.

The ideal arrangement of instruments in a kiln without quick reversal is to have a recorder with its bulbs in what is normally the inlet air passage, with an ordinary hygrometer alongside them, and a second hygrometer in the outlet passage for use during periods of running on reverse circulation. The conditions in the kiln should be controlled to give the correct readings on whichever hygrometer is on the inlet side.

The recorder may, of course, be used for actual readings when the bulbs are on the inlet side, provided that it is checked from time to time by comparison with the nearby hygrometer, and adjustments made when necessary. Such adjustments should only be carried out after making sure that both the wet bulbs are in perfect condition and after the kiln has been running for some time and kept steady for at least a quarter of an hour.

In practice the ideal is seldom attained and all too often an operator has to rely on a single recorder as the only means of determining the temperature and, more important, relative humidity within a kiln holding a valuable load of timber. Whenever this is the case the need for periodic checking, and, when necessary recalibration of the instrument, is obvious. If a hygrometer is not immediately available a quick check on the accuracy of a recorder for measuring relative humidity can be obtained by temporarily removing the sleeve from the wet-bulb when, if all is well, the wet-bulb pen will rise to give exactly the same reading as the dry-bulb.

It is preferable, however, to recalibrate recorders periodically by removing the bulbs from their mountings and immersing them in constantly stirred hot water (around 60°C) whose true temperature is measured by an accurate thin stem mercury-in-glass thermometer. After 10 minutes, if there is any discrepancy between the readings of the instrument and the thermometer, the pen arm can be adjusted by small screws on the arm or its pivot. If the discrepancy is more than 2 or 3°C the manufacturer of the instrument should be called in to service or repair it.

Nearly all kiln recording instruments consist of sensitive elements or bulbs connected by long capillary tubing, encased in some form of protective sheathing, to spiral elements mounted inside the instrument case. The tube system is filled either with mercury, gas or liquid and vapour, and a temperature change of the bulb causes a pressure change and hence a movement of the free end of the spiral element which in turn pushes a pen arm over a chart mounted on a 1-day or a 7-day clock. *Plate 17.*

The elevation of the bulbs relative to the recording instrument affects the readings in the case of the mercury- and the vapour-filled types, so that if the bulbs are not going to be mounted level with the instrument the latter should be calibrated under the actual conditions in which it will be used.

As an alternative to mercury, spirit, or vapour type thermometers, electric resistance type thermometers can be used for either indicating or recording kiln conditions. Partly off-setting the higher price of these is the fact that cables from the elements in the kiln can readily be taken to any convenient central indicating and controlling station as is done in the largest kiln installation in the UK.

Special fittings are usually provided with each recording instrument for mounting the two bulbs and for supplying water to the wet-bulb. *Plate 17a.* When fixing up the bulb holder and water box, a space should be left between them and the kiln wall so that air can pass freely over both bulbs. If a bulb is too close to the kiln wall its temperature may be affected by radiation, whether the wall is cooler or whether it is made hotter by an adjacent kiln running at an appreciably higher temperature. The general rules for the positioning of ordinary hygrometers apply also to recorder bulbs, except, of course, that the latter can be placed well along the length of the air passages if the lengths of capillaries permit.

There are many different systems of feeding water to the wet-bulb. In many of them, wicks or the tails of fabric coverings dip into a shallow trough in which a constant level of water is maintained from a larger tank or an inverted cylinder outside the kiln. In others, a larger reservoir is used inside the kiln; this is fitted with a float valve and supplied from a tank at a higher level outside, into which condensate is fed.

In another and very effective type of wet-bulb arrangement, a cylindrical sleeve made of a porous porcelain-like substance takes the place of the normal fabric material. Mains water is fed through a filter into the sleeve and as it seeps through the material it evaporates and causes the normal wet-bulb depression. In hard water districts the porous sleeves tend to get clogged with chalk and it is necessary periodically to remove and clean them by immersion in dilute hydrochloric acid ('spirits of salts') followed by thorough washing in clean water.

If the instrument must be mounted on a kiln wall, an air space should be left behind the case, for in the mercury or gas-filled types any appreciable increase of the air temperature inside the case tends to alter the reading.

Recording instruments will give long service if due care is exercised when changing the charts and inking the pens. They should be returned to the manufacturers for repair if any serious error develops which cannot be rectified by calibration and adjustment of the pen arms. Trouble is sometimes experienced from the pens failing to mark or tracing too thick a line. When this occurs, pens should be removed for cleaning; soaking in methylated spirits is usually effective.

When a pen of the box type fails to write it may sometimes be cleared by filling to the brim and pressing the top with the ball of the thumb. If this fails, the blockage in the capillary can usually be removed by use of the fine wire provided for the purpose by makers of the instrument. The slit in the end of pens of the V-type should be cleaned out periodically, not with a penknife but by drawing a piece of thin paper through it.

6.4 Automatic control instruments

In most modern kiln installations each kiln is fitted with an instrument which will automatically control the air conditions to any desired temperature and humidity. Direct-acting (or 'self-contained') valve/thermostats have been used but the majority of controllers take the form of recording thermometers with additional systems incorporated which operate valves in the heating and steam-spray feed pipes, a few by hydraulic pressure but most either by compressed air or by electrical means. Many of the controllers are now made to operate the vents also and ensure that no steam is wasted by the steam spray being brought on whilst the vents are open.

In the earlier kilns, automatic controllers used in this country were mostly recorder-controllers employing pneumatically operated diaphragm valves. In recent years there has been a change to the use of electrically-operated equipment which, though rather less reliable, is appreciably cheaper and of a more compact design. Again, although motorised valves for the latter are rather less liable to fail, solenoid valves are used because they are cheaper and in the event of power failure shut off all steam. All types keep the temperature and humidity at any desired levels by controlling the wet- and dry-bulb temperatures.

Full instructions for the installation and use of controllers are issued by the makers but it is usually best to call in service engineers for anything but simple adjustments and maintenance such as the cleaning of filters etc. On the other hand, it is well for an operator to know how any instrument in his care functions. Instruments differ in details of design but the general principle is the same and in the case of the air operated equipment is illustrated by the following description of the temperature controller shown schematically in Figure 13.

A compressed air supply is connected to the instrument through a strainer or drip-well and through a pressure reducer usually set to give an output of clean dry air at about 103 kN/m^2 (15 lbf/in^2). Inside the instrument the flow of air is first restricted by the orifice 1. As the temperature in the kiln rises the Bourdon spiral 2 uncoils and through link 3 and arm 4 raises the circular baffle plate 5 (pivoted about point 6) which was preventing air escaping from nozzle 7. The air pressure in tube 8 falls, the capsule 9 deflates and as the pin and ball valve 10 admits air through tube 11 to the top of the spring loaded diaphragm valve 12 it closes it and the steam flow to the heating coils is cut off. The temperature in the kiln begins to fall and as the pen arm 13 and baffle plate move accordingly the mechanism cuts off air to the diaphragm valve and the spring opens it again. The temperature at

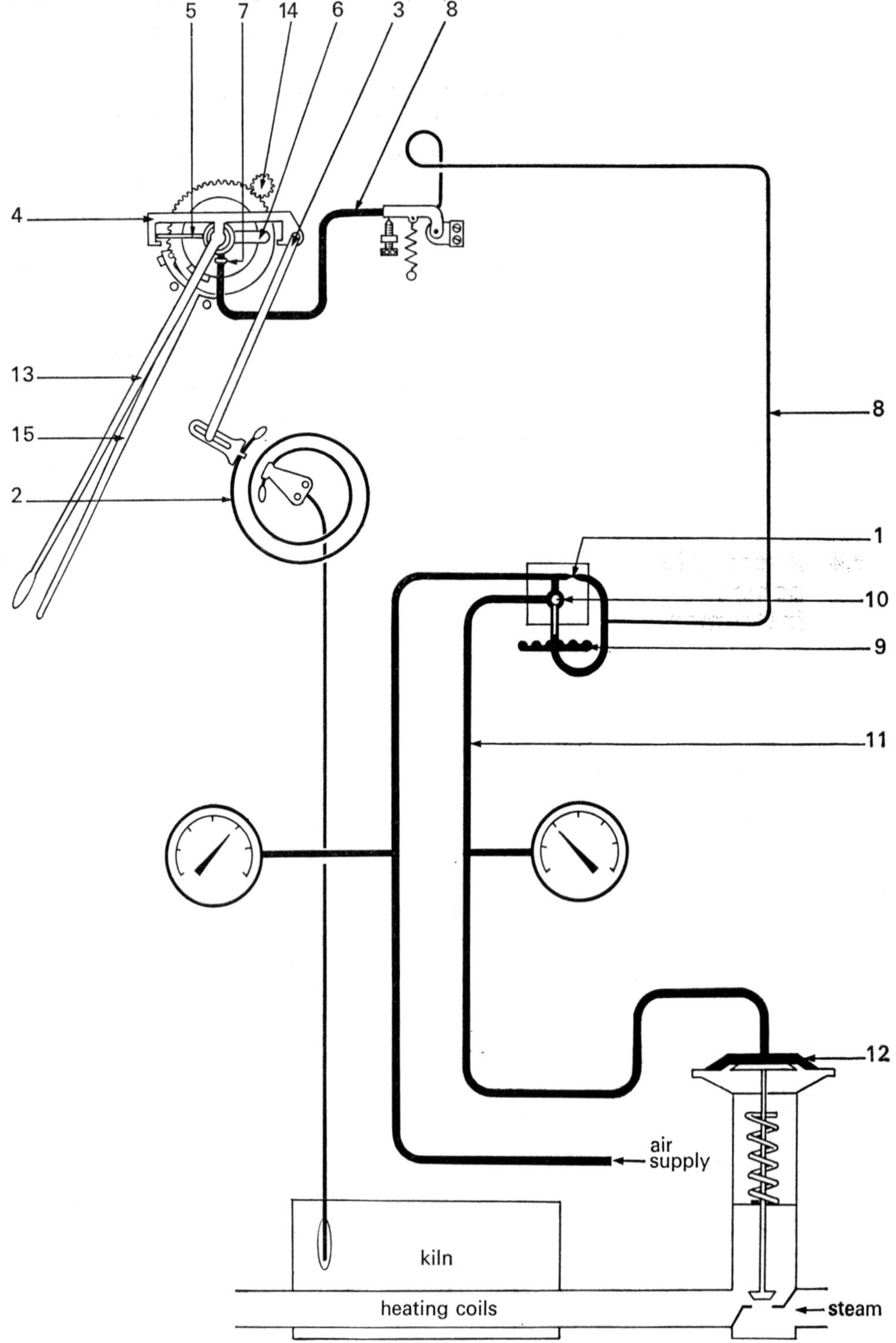

Figure 13 *Schematic diagram of fixed high sensitivity temperature controller*

which the kiln is thus maintained is adjusted by a key and gear 14 altering the position of the setting pointer 15 and of the baffle plate relative to the nozzle.

The controller and valve may be designed so that a fall in temperature causes air to be admitted to the underside of the diaphragm which then opens the valve against the spring. This reverse-acting type has the advantage that in the event of any failure in the compressed air supply all steam to the kiln is automatically cut off.

The diaphragm valves should be mounted in by-passes in the heating and spray feed pipes so that in the event of any defect developing they can be removed for repair and the kiln run on hand control.

The instrument described above is of the high sensitivity type, in which steam is turned full on or right off by the pneumatic system.

There is another main group of kiln controllers in which most of the instruments are rather more complicated and give proportional or throttling control. *Plate 18*. Instead of the air, and hence the valve, being shut right off when the temperature rises slightly above the set point, the air pressure to the valve is slightly reduced and the valve is only partly closed. A nearly steady condition is reached in which the valve 'floats' in such a position that it passes the amount of steam required to maintain the desired temperature.

With the type of electrically-operated controller generally used on kilns the control is of the on-off type. Inside the recorder/controller shown in Plate 19 the spiral element moves a pivoted arm which, as the temperature falls below the set-point, makes contact in a circuit which activates and opens either a solenoid or a motorised valve in the feed pipe to the heating system. This system is duplicated for the wet-bulb spiral to control the steam spray.

Automatic control valves may also be activated through thermostats linked with electrical resistance type thermometers (see 6.3).

In an oil heated type of kiln, the dry-bulb of the controller will cause the oil burner of the air heater to be switched on and off (or to high flame and low flame) and the wet-bulb is made to operate the steam evaporator or the water atomiser.

In timber dryers in which dehumidifiers are used instead of venting, control of humidity is achieved by a humidistat switching the units on and off and a thermostat controls the temperature through the heating elements in the normal manner.

1 Position of controller bulbs or elements

The bulbs or sensing elements of the controller should be fitted up in the same manner as those of a recorder, ie in one of the inlet-side or central air passages. A complication arises, however, when the air circulation is reversed, for the bulbs are then on the outlet side and the instrument will automatically control the heat and spray to give the set conditions there and not in the new inlet air passage. As there is nearly always a temperature drop and a humidity rise across the width of the stack it follows that the inlet temperature will be brought to a higher value and the humidity to a lower one than that desired. Various methods may be employed to overcome this difficulty and it is appropriate to describe them briefly at this point.

Considering first the case of kilns in which the circulation is reversed at intervals of 12 or 24 hours, one of the simplest methods is to re-adjust the set pointers, on reversing, so that the instrument will actually control the air as it comes out of the stack to values such that the condition of the entering air, as indicated by a hygrometer, will be that required by the schedule being applied. When, for example, the inlet temperature is 55°C and the hygrometer on the opposite side indicates 53°C, then on reversal the set pointer should be lowered approximately 2°C to control the new inlet air to 55°C. Some slight further adjustment may be necessary to get the temperature exactly right. Little or no adjustment to the wet-bulb set pointer should be needed as the wet-bulb temperature is virtually the same on both sides of the stack.

In overhead fan kilns a different method of overcoming the difficulty of obtaining correct control, irrespective of the direction of circulation, involves mounting the controller bulbs in a duct below the false ceiling so that air blowing over them is representative of the air entering whichever passage is on the inlet side of the timber stack. The disadvantages of this arrangement are that the wet-bulb in the duct is not easily accessible for inspection during a run, and that instruments of the mercury- or vapour-filled type would have to be mounted at an inconvenient height, or specially calibrated, for the large difference in level between bulbs and instrument.

A third method, adopted in America but not yet to any extent in this country, uses a dual or split bulb system. Two dry-bulbs are fitted, one in the inlet and one in the outlet duct, and the capillaries join up and connect to the one spiral element and indicator in the instrument, which must be of the vapour-filled type. Such a system will automatically record and control on whichever of the bulbs is at the higher temperature, ie the one in the inlet duct. A single wet-bulb in either of the ducts suffices because, as already mentioned, there is practically no change in the wet-bulb temperature of the air as it passes through the timber stack.

Finally there remain to be considered those kilns, of which there are an increasing number, in which the direction of air flow is reversed at very frequent intervals, usually 15 or 30 min. The position of the controller bulbs varies with different makes of kiln. It has been found that, although the bulbs are placed on one side of the kiln load, in the short time they are on the outlet side during reversed flow the changes in the conditions of the inlet air are not great enough to be serious. Controllers used in such an arrangement, however, should preferably be of the proportional response and not of the high sensitivity type.

Another position can be adopted in the side fan horizontal flow type of kiln, for in this the bulbs can, with advantage, be placed in the side passage remote from the fan. In that position they record and control the condition of the air after it has passed through the stack once whichever way the fan is running. The timber on the fan side is subjected first to rather more severe and then to less severe conditions than those set to schedule on the controller, and full benefit is gained from the advantages of quick reversal. Furthermore, access to the bulbs during a run is easier as a small door can readily be provided in the end wall of the passage with no heating pipes to obstruct it.

2 Maintenance of recorder-controllers

The importance of maintaining hygrometers and recorders in good condition, particularly the coverings of their wet-bulbs, is mentioned in 6.2.3. It is even more vital to keep kiln control equipment in perfect condition, especially if they are relied upon to keep kilns on a steady course overnight and during weekends. If the covering of a controller's wet-bulb dries up, the pen will go up to the dry-bulb temperature, causing the instrument to cut off the steam spray entirely, and the humidity may easily fall to a dangerously low level before the fault is discovered. The fall in humidity will be particularly rapid if the vents are also controlled automatically for they will be opened fully as the wet-bulb temperature rises.

A pneumatically operated recorder-controller, used carefully, with a supply of clean, dry, compressed air always ensured by regular blowing down and cleaning of the drip-well, should give satisfactory service over a long period. The instrument makers should be called in to make any major adjustments or recalibration and as some clogging or gradual wear in the system is almost inevitable, they should be asked to overhaul each instrument every two or three years.

In electrically operated controllers, contacts and relays occasionally have to be serviced or replaced and solenoid valves which fail to open or close need repair or replacement. It is advisable to stock spare solenoid coils and valves.

6.5 Fully automatic kiln control

Whilst the automatic kiln controllers already described (6.4) effectively maintain pre-determined wet- and dry-bulb temperatures in the kiln, their settings have to be re-adjusted manually from time to time as the timber dries so that the air conditions in the kiln conform to the chosen schedule. The operator therefore needs to know the moisture content of the load he is dealing with and in the majority of cases this involves the periodic weighing of kiln samples.

The aim of a fully automatic system is to relieve the operator of this routine and moreover to take charge of the entire drying operation. From settings made at the start of the run, such equipment is designed to warm up the kiln, adjust kiln temperatures and/or humidities so as to maintain the required air conditions corresponding with the moisture content of the load and finally to condition and cool down the kiln when the timber reaches the desired final moisture content.

1 Cam controllers

Cam controllers represent the earliest attempt at fully automatic control. They are time-based and depend on the assumption that for a given species and thickness of timber the load moisture content, and hence the air conditions needed in the kiln, will depend on the length of time drying has been in progress. Specially cut cams are used to set the wet- and dry-bulb temperatures to the appropriate values as drying proceeds. Different cams have to be cut for different species and thicknesses but their main disadvantage is that there is no direct link between the controller and the moisture content of the timber. A load drying more slowly than usual could easily be shut down before it was properly dry and it is advisable to check for correct moisture content in the later stages of the run.

Systems developed in Europe and America represent an advance on the cam controller in that their operation is related to the moisture content of the load. This they determine continuously either by means of electrical moisture meters or by weighing the load.

2 Controllers based on electrical determination of moisture content

In these controllers, instead of the removable samples used in normal kiln operation, temperature corrected moisture meters and stainless steel probes are employed to measure the moisture content of selected boards in the load.

One such system with a control panel as shown in Plate 20 provides for a two-step temperature schedule and adjusts the relative humidity continuously as the timber dries. A constant ratio, selected initially according to the species and thickness of timber being dried, is automatically maintained between the load moisture content and the EMC of the kiln air. The latter is monitored by measuring electrically the moisture content of a wafer of wood (*Plate 21*) which responds relatively quickly to the kiln air conditions.

The automatic equipment can be set to control the warming up, the application of a conditioning treatment and the cooling of the kiln.

With resistance-based moisture determination, changes in kiln air conditions are brought about somewhat slowly above 30 per cent moisture content and there is also a tendency to over-dry the load slightly. Nevertheless systems of this kind can dry many species of timber to an acceptable standard and are in commercial use in Europe.

3 Controllers based on moisture content by weight

With this system, load cells are arranged to weigh the load (or part of it) and the initial weight is related to initial moisture content by cutting a few typical boards for moisture content in the usual way. Again, this information, together with details of the schedule to be followed and the final moisture content required, is fed into the controller at the start of the run and the system then takes complete control of the whole drying operation.

This method of determining moisture content is effective over the complete range from green downwards, but in its usual form provides information on average moisture content only and gives no indication of possible board to board variation in the load. The duration of any conditioning treatment therefore has to be decided on the basis of prior experience with similar material. Control systems based on weight are currently in experimental use.

Fully automatic control systems, whether based on weight or electrical determination are considerably more expensive than the ordinary recorder/controller. Their higher initial cost, however, may in some circumstances be offset by savings in operator's time and possible better utilisation of kiln capacity.

Chapter 7
Operation of a kiln

Although equipment (6.4, 6.5) which will automatically control the air conditions is fitted to nearly all new kilns and has been added to existing plant, there will be for some years to come a number of manually operated kilns in which fully satisfactory results can be obtained by good operators. To save repetition, steps which are common to both manual and automatic operation are dealt with together.

7.1 Preliminaries to a kiln run

It is assumed that the timber has been loaded into the kiln and, the initial moisture content of samples having been determined, the initial kiln conditions have been decided (see 9.3, 9.4).

Before starting up a kiln the operator should ensure that, as far as is practicable, all gaps in and around the pile which would allow short-circuiting of air through them have been sealed, that the bearings on the fan shafts are greased or oiled and that the fans, belt drives etc, are in good order.

The hygrometer(s) should next be placed in position, new sleeves and wicks fitted on recorder or controller wet-bulbs and a chart put on the recorder. The fans may now be started and warming of the kiln begun.

7.2 Warming up

Steam valves should be opened gradually at first in order to prevent water-hammer, but as soon as the water has been cleared from the heating system the valves may all be turned full on, as no harm should result from a fairly rapid warming of the load.

During the warming, the temperature of the wood will lag appreciably behind that of the air and consequently the humidity of the air as it cools in passing between the layers of timber will be increased. It has frequently been found that if the warming is done reasonably fast, moisture is condensed on the timber surfaces and the moisture content, even of green timber, is increased slightly. For this reason, it is not recommended that a steaming treatment be given or a very high humidity employed during the initial warming period.

It is suggested that, as a rough guide, a constant difference of 5°C (9°F) between wet- and dry-bulb readings should be maintained until the desired dry-bulb temperature is attained when, of course, the wet-bulb reading should be set according to the schedule selected.

With automatically-controlled kilns, the dry-bulb pointer may be set to the final running temperature and all coils turned on, the steam spray valve being adjusted by hand to maintain the 5°C difference between wet- and dry-bulb readings. To save the operator's time, however, particularly when automatically-controlled kilns are run only during the daytime, the controller may be set to the running temperatures on both wet- and dry-bulbs and the kiln left to warm up by itself.

As the desired dry-bulb temperature is approached when on hand control, the number of heating coils in use should be reduced. If this adjustment is left too late, the temperature will overshoot the mark, for a coil does not cease to give off heat immediately the valve in the feed pipe is closed. The humidity, on the other hand, responds fairly quickly to changes in valve setting on the steam spray. It must be remembered that with some recorders there will be a lag in the temperature readings during warming, especially in that indicated by a wet-bulb covered with a moist porous sleeve.

7.3 Steady running

The actual manipulation of the valves to obtain any set of conditions in a kiln will be found to be fairly easy after a certain amount of practice. In general, the dry-bulb temperature is controlled by the number of coils used and the amount and pressure of the steam admitted to those coils. The wet-bulb temperature is regulated by the amount of live steam passed through the valve to the steam spray and into the circulating air, and also, at times, by the adjustment of dampers in the ventilators. It will be found, however, that the controls of the two temperatures are not independent of each other. For example, if the dry-bulb reading is right and the wet-bulb is low, turning up the spray to increase the latter will also raise the dry-bulb temperature somewhat, and it will be necessary to turn down a heating valve slightly. On the other hand, any cutting down of the steam spray or opening of the vents in order to lower the wet-bulb temperature will also result in a small drop in the dry-bulb temperature unless the heating is increased slightly.

In a kiln designed to be manually controlled the heating pipes are usually divided into groups or banks of differing numbers of pipes, say 2, 4, 6 and 8 (plain pipes) each with a separate valve and steam trap. It is sound practice to have one, or a combination, of these banks full on, and, if the temperature is then much higher than that required, to control on a master valve of a reseat type. Too many pipes should not be used, since the valve would have to be almost closed in order to keep the temperature down, and excessive wear may occur. Furthermore, there will be a tendency for part of the coils to become waterlogged, and appreciable temperature differences along the length of the kiln may result. This applies to some extent to kilns which are automatically controlled, particularly those with proportional response type instruments. The number of coils brought into operation here should be rather greater, but not too much greater, than that required to give the desired temperature when the coils are all fully opened. In this manner it can be ensured that with the throttling type of controller the valve will float in, say, a quarter or one-third open position, and will not be just off the seating.

The operator must soon learn from experience which coil or combination of coils to use for any particular set of conditions. He has less need of this, however, in running modern kilns in which the heating system is perhaps over-simplified, consisting only of one or two banks of large diameter gilled pipes. These are usually controlled by the electrically operated type of instrument through valves which are either shut or fully open so that 'wire-drawing' never occurs. The fluctuations in temperature as will be seen on the recorder charts are greater as a result and the operator will have to adjust the setting arms so that the mid-line of the 'saw-tooth' trace is on the desired schedule temperature.

It should always be remembered in operating a kiln that the relative humidity of the air is the most important factor in the control of drying and that running a kiln 5 or 10 per cent low in humidity in the initial stages may easily result in excessive checking of the timber. Departures of 2°C or 3°C from the schedule in temperature, on the other hand, will not have any great effect on the drying.

It follows therefore that it is far more important to maintain the correct difference between the wet- and dry-bulb readings than to maintain the exact dry-bulb temperature given in the schedule. Take for example, the case of a kiln load which is being dried to Schedule C (*Appendix B*) and when the conditions required are: dry-bulb 40·5°C, wet-bulb 38·0°C giving a relative humidity of 85 per cent. If, after valve adjustments, the kiln settles to 42°C dry-bulb and 39·5°C wet-bulb, it is not worth making any change, for the humidity is then 85½ per cent, ie only ½ per cent high. If the hygrometer readings were 42°C and 38°C however, the humidity would be only 76½ per cent and the heating and steam spray should at once be adjusted to reduce the difference between the wet- and dry-bulbs to 2½°C.

So far, little has been said about the third means available of controlling humidity conditions in a kiln, viz adjustments of the vents through which air interchange is effected. Ideally the vents should be brought into use only when it is found that with the steam spray shut right off the humidity rises above the value required. The vents should then be opened so that a certain amount of hot, damp air is exhausted and cool air drawn in, which, when heated, lowers the humidity of the resulting mixture of air and vapour being circulated.

It is sometimes found that in runs on slow drying loads the vents need never be opened. This can only be due to the fact that the moisture evaporated from the wood is escaping from the kiln by inadvertent leakage through badly fitting doors and/or by condensation on poorly insulated walls and roof.

It is obviously very wasteful of steam to open the vents much more than is actually necessary, for this will mean that the steam spray will have to be increased in order to maintain the required humidity. Most operators find that the best control of humidity is obtained by opening the vents just slightly more than is necessary for getting rid of the water extracted from the timber at any given stage of the drying, and then making good the deficit by means of the steam spray, which can usually be adjusted to a finer degree than the air-interchange vents. The ideal amount to open the vents of any particular kiln can only be judged by experience.

Many modern kilns are fitted with instruments which control the kiln vents as well as the heating and spray. This effects a saving in steam which is important, for instance, where there is only a limited supply or the boilers use expensive fuel. In pneumatically-operated control systems, compressed air is made to operate the dampers by means of a diaphragm lever motor. When the wet-bulb temperature rises above the desired value the spray is shut off, and then, if necessary, the vents are opened. Conversely, when the wet-bulb temperature drops below the set point, the dampers are closed before the steam spray is brought into operation. In simple electrically-operated controllers there are two contacts activated by the wet-bulb arm movement and there is a period when neither spray nor vents are brought into action.

It is worth repeating here the warning that with automatically-controlled vents in operation, the drying up of the wet-bulb covering can be all the more serious because not only will the spray be shut off but also the vents will open to their full extent and the humidity will drop fairly rapidly. Frequent checks on the water supply system and the condition of the wet-bulb covering should therefore be made.

The operation of kilns heated by other means will obviously differ in detail but the general principles are similar to those in steam-heated units.

In low temperature drying rooms or driers employing dehumidifiers, humidistats using hair, treated paper, or other elements, may be employed to control the relative humidity.

7.4 Kiln routine

Apart from warming up a kiln and keeping it at the required conditions, the routine of kiln operation during a run consists mainly of weighing samples and calculating their estimated moisture contents, changing charts, keeping records, and making changes in temperature and humidity as dictated by the schedule followed and by the state of the load generally.

Towards the end of the kiln run a conditioning treatment (see 9.2.3) may be found necessary and should be continued until final moisture content checks have shown the load to be satisfactorily dried. A casehardening relief treatment as described in 9.2.4 may also be required before the kiln is cooled.

When drying to a very precise moisture content specification it is advisable to carry out the casehardening relief a day or two before the end of the run so that time is available for a conditioning treatment to be applied following any moisture gain resulting from the relief treatment.

7.5 Cooling

At the end of the kiln run, loads of some species can be withdrawn immediately without any great risk of their being damaged as they cool outside. This is not, however, to be recommended as general practice, particularly if the kiln is running at a high temperature. The timber retains its heat for a considerable time and cooler air passing between the layers of the pile will become appreciably warmer and therefore drier. This may lead to a renewal of casehardening stresses and at the worst might cause the timber to surface check.

When the load is such that it can safely be withdrawn whilst still hot, a worthwhile saving in time and steam can be achieved during a succession of short runs by running a fresh load immediately into the hot kiln. It is important that the dried loads should be allowed to cool completely under cover or protected by tarpaulins or polythene sheets, before they are machined (see 9.3).

Theoretically the air humidity should be kept high during the cooling period but, unfortunately, use of the steam spray tends to prolong the process unduly as it also adds heat. (In this respect some advantage is held by kilns fitted with cold water sprays.) As a compromise, a difference of not more than 5°C (9°F) between wet- and dry-bulb readings should be maintained until the temperature has dropped to within about 20°C of that of the outside atmosphere, when the kiln can be opened up and the load withdrawn.

Even this degree of control in cooling is often difficult to put into practice and a further alternative is to raise the humidity for a short time (if a casehardening relief treatment is not already in progress) and then shut off all steam, switch off the fans and leave the kiln to cool without further attention. Operators who have to dry to exact moisture contents will learn to allow for the drop of 1 per cent or so which nearly always occurs during cooling.

In a small number of kiln plants, steam is available only during the day-time so the kilns cool down overnight and have to be rewarmed each morning. When the load consists of a fresh-sawn, freely-drying timber, the fans may with advantage be left running overnight and the vents left open, provided that the heating pipes and steam supply are sufficient to effect rapid warming next morning. On the other hand, in

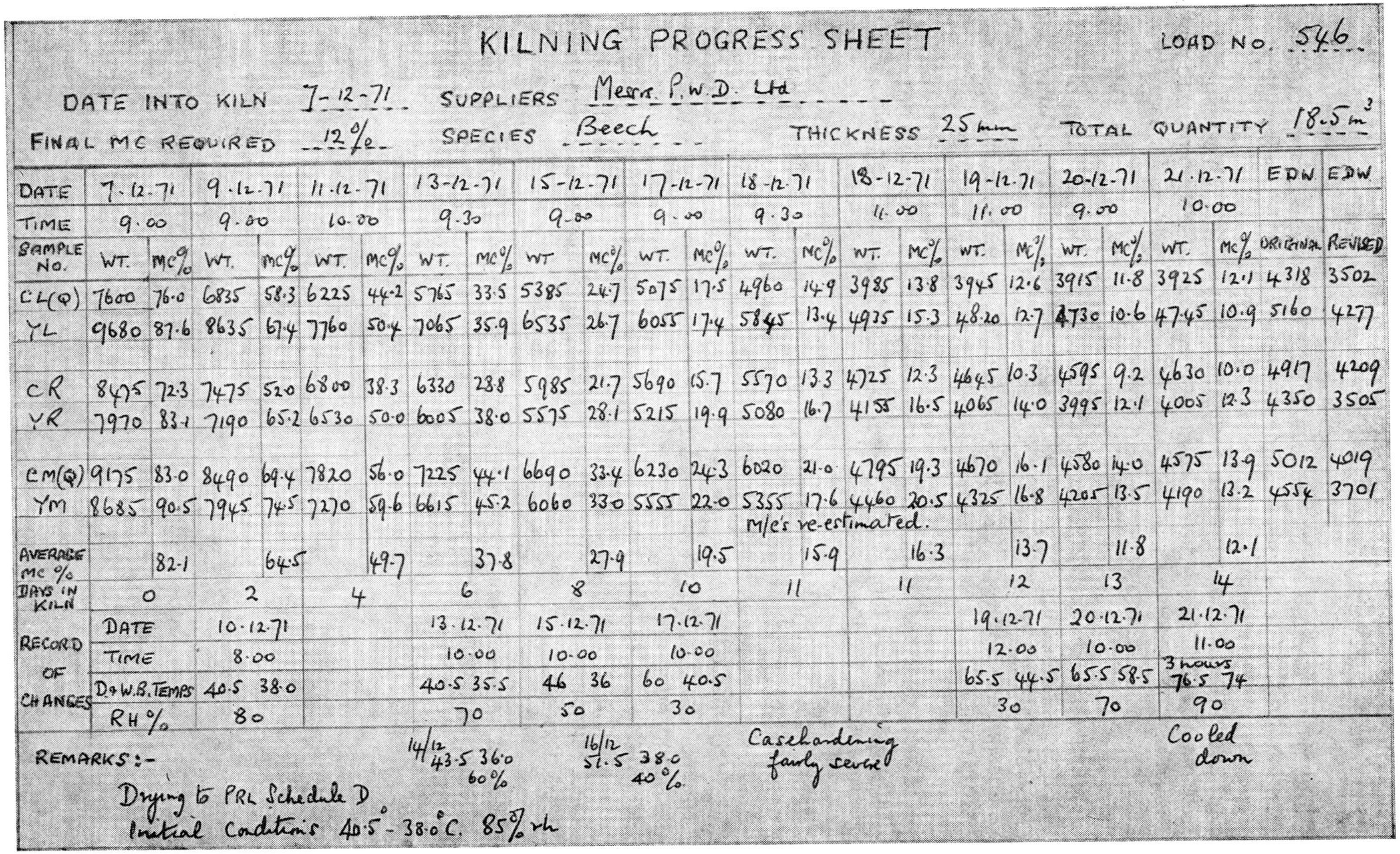

KILNING PROGRESS SHEET — LOAD NO. 546

DATE INTO KILN 7-12-71 SUPPLIERS Messrs P.W.D. Ltd

FINAL MC REQUIRED 12% SPECIES Beech THICKNESS 25 mm TOTAL QUANTITY 18.5 m³

DATE	7.12.71		9.12.71		11.12.71		13.12.71		15.12.71		17.12.71		18.12.71		18.12.71		19.12.71		20.12.71		21.12.71		EDW	EDW
TIME	9.00		9.00		10.00		9.30		9.00		9.00		9.30		11.00		11.00		9.00		10.00			
SAMPLE NO.	WT.	MC%	WT.	MC%	WT.	MC%	WT.	MC%	WT.	MC%	WT.	MC%	WT.	MC%	WT.	MC%	WT.	MC%	WT.	MC%	WT.	MC%	ORIGINAL	REVISED
CL(Q)	7600	76.0	6835	58.3	6225	44.2	5765	33.5	5385	24.7	5075	17.5	4960	14.9	3985	13.8	3945	12.6	3915	11.8	3925	12.1	4318	3502
YL	9680	87.6	8635	67.4	7760	50.4	7065	35.9	6535	26.7	6055	17.4	5845	13.4	4935	15.3	4820	12.7	4730	10.6	4745	10.9	5160	4277
CR	8475	72.3	7475	52.0	6800	38.3	6330	28.8	5985	21.7	5690	15.7	5570	13.3	4725	12.3	4645	10.3	4595	9.2	4630	10.0	4917	4209
YR	7970	83.1	7190	65.2	6530	50.0	6005	38.0	5575	28.1	5215	19.9	5080	16.7	4155	16.5	4065	14.0	3995	12.1	4005	12.3	4350	3505
CM(Q)	9175	83.0	8490	69.4	7820	56.0	7225	44.1	6690	33.4	6230	24.3	6020	21.0	4795	19.3	4670	16.1	4580	14.0	4575	13.9	5012	4019
YM	8685	90.5	7945	74.5	7270	59.6	6615	45.2	6060	33.0	5555	22.0	5355	17.6	4460	20.5	4325	16.8	4205	13.5	4190	13.2	4554	3701
													M/c's re-estimated.											
AVERAGE MC %		82.1		64.5		49.7		37.8		27.9		19.5		15.9		16.3		13.7		11.8		12.1		
DAYS IN KILN	0		2		4		6		8		10		11		11		12		13		4			

RECORD OF CHANGES							
DATE	10.12.71	13.12.71	15.12.71	17.12.71	19.12.71	20.12.71	21.12.71
TIME	8.00	10.00	10.00	10.00	12.00	10.00	11.00
D & W.B. TEMPS	40.5 38.0	40.5 35.5	46 36	60 40.5	65.5 44.5	65.5 58.5	3 hours 76.5 74
RH %	80	70	50	30	30	70	90

REMARKS:- 14/12 43.5 36.0 60% 16/12 51.5 38.0 40% Casehardening fairly severe Cooled down

Drying to PRL Schedule D

Initial Conditions 40.5 – 38.0°C. 85% rh

Figure 14 *Record of a kiln run*

the later stages of a run or with check-susceptible, slow-drying timbers the fans should be switched off and the vents closed.

Intermittent drying causes less loss in time than might be expected for during the shut-down period some movement of moisture from the warmer, wetter interior of the wood takes place and so moisture gradients tend to be less steep and satisfactory results are obtained. However, it will nearly always be found to be more economical to make fuller use of the kilns by providing a continuous supply of steam from, for example, an automatic oil-fired boiler.

7.6 Difficulties that may arise in kiln operation

Various difficulties may be encountered in kiln operation, often perhaps due to faults developing in the kiln plant or the instruments. An efficient operator should be able to trace these faults and correct many of them himself. The chart (pp 56-7) lists the symptoms and possible causes of such troubles (see also 8.6); the remedies are usually self-evident.

7.7 Kiln records

It is most desirable that an operator should make a careful record of the progress of every run, so that at any particular time the condition and behaviour of the load can be judged.

These records, properly filed, provide very useful information to an operator when, at a later date, he has to undertake the drying of similar loads. He can, for example, decide from the records how long a run is likely to take, whether he can expedite the process by an alteration in schedule, and how best he can avoid such troubles as may have been experienced in previous runs. Finally, records are often of value in answering any queries that may arise later as to the treatment given, or the initial and final condition and moisture content of any particular load. Kiln instrument charts should be kept to supplement data in the record sheets.

Various forms of record sheets have been devised and typical of these is the example shown in Figure 14. This (meant only as a guide) records particulars of a kiln run on 25 mm (1 in) home grown beech.

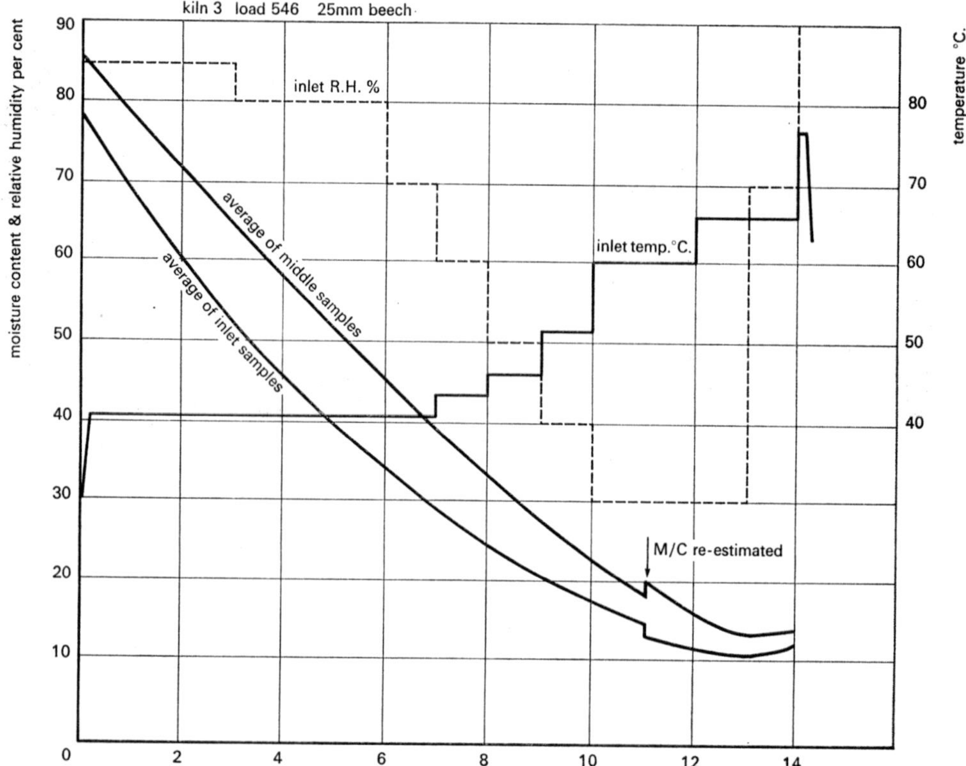

Figure 15 *Graphical record of a kiln run*

The graphical representation of the data on the record sheet as shown in Figure 15 is not called for in normal kiln operation, but can be helpful when carrying out trials on new timbers, new kilns or the modification of existing schedules.

It is a good idea to place boards or slates near the control instruments in each kiln, on which to record brief details of the load and the current schedule conditions. To assist in the planning of loads and smooth running of a large battery, some form of central kiln progress indicator board should be devised.

Difficulties which may arise in the operation of a kiln

Symptoms	Possible causes	Remarks
Dry-bulb temperature cannot be attained.	1 Improper design of heating system, eg: a Insufficient heating surface; b Coils of different lengths leading to one trap.	
	2 Heating coil/s waterlogged by: a Strainer/s being blocked with dirt; b Trap/s failing to eject condensate.	Outlet pipe/s cold
	3 Steam in coils at low pressure due to trap letting live steam pass.	Dirt between trap valve and seating.
	4 Steam supply insufficient or too low in pressure.	
	5 Lack of circulation, eg owing to power failure.	
	6 Badly leaking doors.	
Dry-bulb temperature correct but wet-bulb temperature cannot be attained.	1 Vents opened unnecessarily or too widely.	
	2 Insufficient steam spray.	Either higher pressure steam, more holes in the pipe, or a second spray pipe required.
Dry-bulb temperature cannot be kept down to required value.	1 Valves to heating pipes letting steam pass when closed.	
	2 An adjacent kiln running at a much higher temperature.	
Dry-bulb temperature difficult to control at low values.	Too many pipes in use.	Use smallest coil available.
Wet-bulb temperature cannot be kept down to required value.	1 Vents not opened sufficiently or too small.	
	2 Valve to steam spray letting steam through when closed.	Detected by turning off fans and listening.
	3 Leak in heating pipes.	Detected by turning off fans and spray and listening.

	4 False reading due to drying or partial drying of wet-bulb covering.	
Both temperatures fluctuating.	Boiler pressure fluctuating, and either no pressure reducing valve fitted or reducer not functioning properly.	
Dry-bulb temperature only fluctuating.	Water getting on to dry-bulb of instrument.	eg by condensation drips from ceiling or vents above it.
Differences in air conditions (and hence in drying rate) along the length of the kiln.	1 Local overheating due to cluster of feed pipes inside kiln, or to adjacent boiler room or warm operating room at end opposite doors.	Lag feed pipes.
	2 Partial waterlogging of the coils.	
	3 Leak in heating pipe.	
	4 Some holes in spray pipe blocked.	
	5 Uneven air circulation due to fan loose on shaft, or driving belt/s off or slipping.	
	6 Excessive heat loss through large doors.	
	7 Cold air entering through badly leaking doors.	
Differences in conditions up and down the height of the kiln	Faulty air circulation as a result of:	
	1 Air short-circuiting the pile.	
	2 Motor trouble or belt slip.	
Water on surfaces of kiln piles	1 Condensation causing dripping of water from kiln ceiling.	Insulation of roof should be improved.
	2 Condensation causing dripping of water from outlet vents.	False ceiling should be made water-tight and drained.
	3 Leak in steam coil.	
	4 Badly placed or insufficiently drained steam spray pipe.	

Chapter 8 Maintenance and testing of kilns

Whilst it may be necessary to call upon specialists for certain items of maintenance or overhaul of kiln plant, the operator should be capable of carrying out minor running repairs himself and should also keep the kiln buildings and equipment in good condition. A clean, tidy plant and operating room (such as that illustrated in Plate 22) is usually an indication of keenness and efficiency in kiln operation.

It is proposed to deal in turn with the various items of maintenance which should receive special attention from the operator.

8.1 Air circulation system

1 Fans and fan drives

The fans, and the system of shafts and motors driving them, obviously need attention to avoid breakdowns, and the first priority is to keep the bearings well greased. Bearings situated inside the kiln and so subjected to high temperatures and humidities need special attention. They are usually of the totally enclosed ball or roller bearing type, and a special, high melting point grease should be used. If a pressure gun is employed, bearings should not be packed too tightly with grease or they may be inclined to run hot.

Owing to the large temperature range to which a kiln is subjected, considerable thermal movement of the fan shafting occurs, over 13 mm ($\frac{1}{2}$ in) in long kilns of the longitudinal shaft type. It is therefore important to examine the ball races at regular intervals to ensure that they are free in their housings to move with the expansion and contraction of the shaft.

Belt drives need regular attention; the V-belts or flat belts, as the case may be, must be taken up when slack and replaced whenever necessary. Belt-slip in the fan drives has often been found responsible for poor results in a drying run. Chain drives cannot cause this particular trouble but they should also be inspected at regular intervals.

The fans themselves should be examined occasionally, for a fan may possibly work loose on a shaft though this rarely occurs if the initial fitting is carried out properly.

2 Air vents

All dampers in the air exhaust and intake chimneys or ducts should be kept well oiled or greased. The outlet dampers are inevitably subjected to corrosive conditions caused by condensation of the hot, damp air and if the moving parts are of corrodable material they will soon rust and become immovable unless attended to at regular intervals.

In some ventilating systems, the dampers are linked to a remote control by means of cable and pulleys. The gear should be inspected periodically to make sure that the vents do actually open to the extent shown on the indicators, and when a number of butterfly dampers are linked by cable, occasional inspection is especially desirable as they may get out of phase.

8.2 Heating system

1 Pipes

The efficiency of heating pipes depends very largely on proper provision being made for the drainage of condensate from them. There should be a continuous fall from the feed end to the outlet end and the operator should check to make sure that no sagging has occurred which might lead to the formation of pockets of condensate.

2 Steam traps

The correct arrangement and proper functioning of steam traps are vital factors in the maintenance of maximum efficiency in a heating system. Traps must be capable of rapidly removing the condensate from the heating coils, and also any air introduced into them with the steam. Ideally, there should be a separate steam trap for each coil. The trap should be located below the coil it has to drain; it should be large enough to handle the condensate formed in the coil and should be of the correct type for the range of pressures employed. To prevent dirt getting into traps, strainers are fitted just in front of them, and one of the regular maintenance jobs on a kiln is to take out and clean the gauze or perforated cylinder in each strainer, the frequency of doing so depending on the cleanliness of the steam supply.

To avoid any back pressure from the main condensate return affecting the trap, check or swing values ('non-return' values) are placed between this pipe and the traps. Some kiln engineers also fit drain cocks, the opening of which makes it possible to determine readily whether the traps are working properly.

It is fairly obvious when a trap is not getting rid of condensate, for the trap and the pipe leading to it will soon become relatively cold. It is not so easy, however, to tell when a trap is failing to shut properly and so letting by some steam. A sight glass may be fitted below each trap so that it can be seen whether it is functioning correctly.

It may be mentioned that it is usually possible to hear whether traps are functioning properly, by placing the head of a screwdriver on the body of the trap and the handle against the ear, when the alternate flushing and shutting off may be heard.

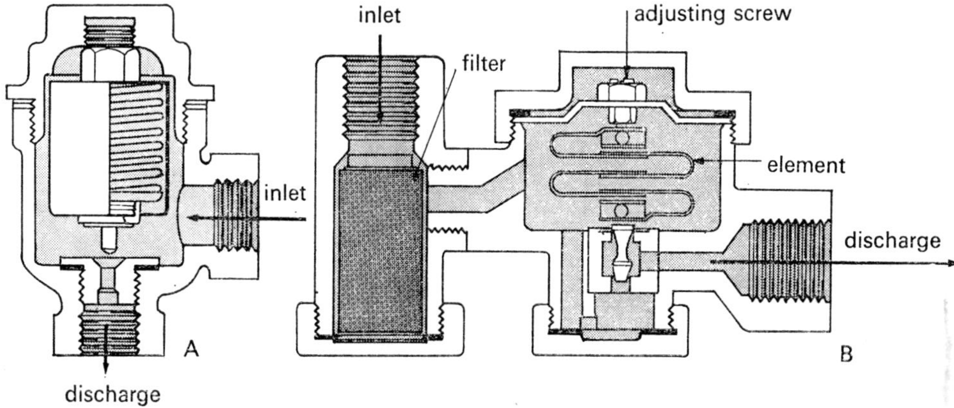

Figure 16 *Thermostatic steam traps*

Since the steam traps play an important part in the heating and control of a kiln, the operator should himself be able to maintain them in good working order and it is proposed to describe briefly the various types that are commonly fitted. There are two main classes of trap, thermostatic and gravity, but in some traps both mechanisms are employed and in others the traps are operated thermodynamically by flash steam.

Thermostatic traps, as their name implies, operate by the action of an element which expands and contracts with changes of temperature. This

element usually takes the form of a helical tube filled with a volatile liquid, as in the trap illustrated in Figure 16a, but in the thermostatic type of trap shown in Figure 16b a bimetallic element is employed. When relatively cool condensate surrounds the element, it is contracted and lifts the valve clear of the seating so that water (and any air present) passes out through the trap. When all the condensate is discharged and steam enters the trap, the rise in temperature causes the element to expand, so closing the valve. When condensate accumulates again, the temperature drops and the valve opens, and this cycle is repeated at fairly frequent intervals.

For ease of maintenance, all traps should be placed outside the kiln chamber, and the thermostatic type will obviously function better outside since cooling will be quicker and the traps will open more often. The manufacturers usually recommend that a short vertical length of pipe should be inserted between the end of the heating coil and the trap so that condensate can collect and cool in the pipe rather than in the coil itself.

Whenever a thermostatic trap is found either to be passing live steam or failing to eject condensate, it is a comparatively simple matter to shut off the valve to the coil or coils it is supposed to drain and to dismantle the trap to rectify the trouble. It may be found that the valve is being held open by dirt collected between the valve and the seating, that the valve and seating are worn, or that the thermostatic element is clogged up or faulty. In the latter case a new element can soon be fitted and some spare elements and valve seatings should always be kept in stock.

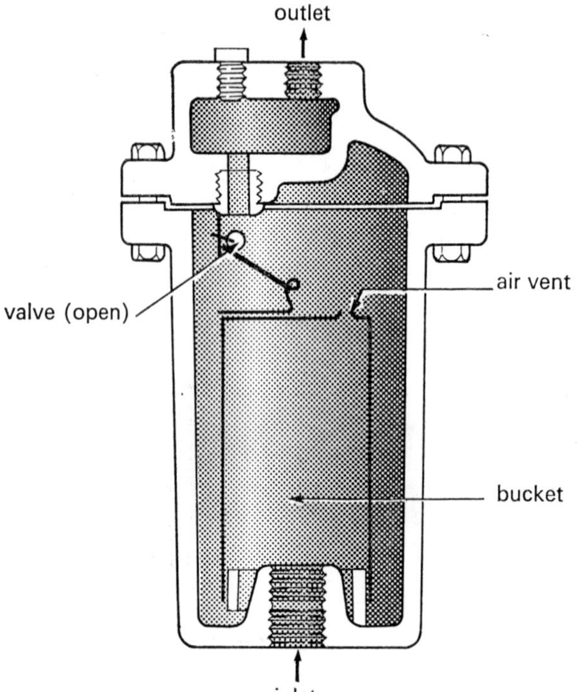

Figure 17
An inverted bucket trap

Gravity traps. There are several types of steam trap which operate by the effect of the weight of water, or of buoyancy, on a bucket or float linked to the outlet valve. In the inverted bucket trap shown in Figure 17, the bucket drops when the trap is full of water and so opens the discharge valve. When steam enters the bucket its buoyancy increases and it rises and closes the outlet. Any air trapped in the bucket escapes through the vent hole provided and, collecting in the top of the trap, is blown out before the condensate is discharged. These bucket traps usually have a self-scouring action and the valve and seating, and also possibly the air vent, should need only very occasional attention. After some years of service, however, the bucket and the linkage to the valve may become worn and call either for new parts or a new trap.

In the open-bucket type of gravity trap the condensate collects in the body of the trap and overflows into the bucket, which eventually sinks and in so doing opens the valve at the top. The trap then discharges until the bucket rises again and closes the valve. There are various designs of this type of trap but they all operate on this general principle. In some of them, a separate valve is provided for venting air and for quickly getting rid of large amounts of condensate when the heating coil which the trap has to drain is first opened.

Traps of the *float* or *tilt* type also need some provision for venting air. In the float trap depicted in Figure 18, an air vent connecting to the outlet of the trap is sealed by a valve and thermostatic element, except when the temperature in the trap body is relatively low.

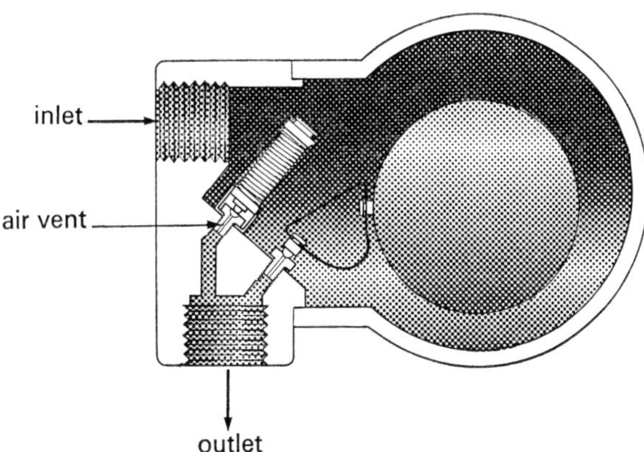

Figure 18 *A float trap*

8.3 Valves

It is obvious that all valves should be kept in good condition. The ease of control depends very largely on the ability to shut off any particular valve effectively and to get an accurate setting readily on the main control valve or on the valve to the smallest coil.

If a closed valve is found to be letting steam pass through, and, on dismantling it, it is found that the trouble is not due to any removable foreign matter but to 'pitting' or 'scoring' of the valve and seat, the difficulty may be overcome by grinding in the valve. If the pitting is too deep for grinding in, either a new valve head and seating or an entirely new valve should be fitted. It is recommended that the main control valve, on which some throttling and hence greater wear is inevitable, should be of the reseat type so that the necessity for complete replacement is avoided.

Other maintenance work on valves includes the occasional tightening up of the gland nut or actual repacking of the stuffing-box round the spindle. Escape of steam and dripping of hot water from the valve are the signs that such attention is needed, and if the valves are overhead the operator may soon be painfully made aware of the desirability of early action.

When valves or traps are removed for repair it is strongly advisable to plug any open-ended pipes on the live steam side in order to eliminate any possible danger from scalding steam should the main valve be accidentally opened.

Reducing valves should give long service without much attention. When they cease to function properly it is usually due to broken springs, deterioration of the diaphragm or sleeve, or in some types of valve to failure of the expansion elements. When this happens, a steam engineer should be called in to make the necessary repairs.

A strainer should be fitted on the inlet side of every reducing valve and, ideally, an excess pressure release valve on the outlet side, if any part of the kiln heating system is rated below the maximum inlet pressure.

8.4 Painting

1 Metalwork

It is most important that the steam pipes, as well as all other ferrous metal parts inside a kiln, should be kept thoroughly painted to protect them from corrosion in the hot, damp atmosphere to which they are exposed. When drying some species of wood, such as oak and sweet chestnut, there are acid extracts in the damp circulating air and the corrosion rate tends to increase.

Whenever the operator finds that the paint on the pipes or other metal parts, such as fans, fan boxes etc, has deteriorated, he should arrange to have their surfaces thoroughly cleaned and repainted at the earliest opportunity. Aluminium paint (two coats) is suitable for the pipes and there are various other heat-resisting paints available. For the 'cold' metalwork a medium grade of bituminous paint has been found to be very satisfactory. In kilns which are in continuous use, painting is often found necessary once every year and it may conveniently be done at the time when the boiler is shut down for cleaning and inspection.

A point to remember during painting of the steam spray pipe is that the jet holes are liable to become blocked. They should be cleared afterwards, or blocking prevented by inserting nails in them whilst painting is in progress.

The pipework outside a kiln is less subject to corrosion but it should be painted and also lagged to cut down heat losses.

In some kilns, wood is used for the construction of fan boxes, baffles etc, and will last longer if painted with a moisture- and heat-proof paint. Non-corrodable screws should be used in repairing any woodwork inside kilns.

2 Walls

The inside brickwork and concrete in a kiln should be protected from corrosion and made as waterproof as possible by a coating of fairly heavy grade bituminous or other suitable paint. If left untreated, the walls will absorb moisture in the early stages of a run when condensation takes place, and in consequence, the heat loss through them will increase appreciably since the conductivity of wet masonry is higher than that of dry. Walls etc, of prefabricated kilns do not require protective painting if the panels are made of high purity aluminium and all direct contact with other metals is avoided so that there is no electrolytic action to cause corrosion.

8.5 Doors

It is most desirable that kiln doors should fit tightly and have good insulating properties. Air leaks round the doors cause differences in the air conditions in their neighbourhood, and poor insulation results in local cooling and excessive condensation. Badly fitting doors have been shown by experiment to cause loss of heat on a surprisingly large scale. In one test the stopping up of all leaks round doors, inspection doors, drains etc, of an internal-fan kiln nearly halved the steam consumption required to maintain the desired conditions.

It will be appreciated, therefore, that particular care should be taken to maintain the doors in a good condition. The synthetic rubber or felt packing-strips fitted round most doors should be repaired or renewed whenever necessary and the jambs adjusted where provision is made for this. Leaks may often be detected by examination from the inside of the kiln with the door shut. Gaps for the rails passing through the door sill should be filled by felted wooden blocks after the load has been run into the kiln.

Some types of carrier door are pressed against the jambs by the weight of the door bearing through projecting lugs on slotted plates at the top and sides. *Plate 23*. The relative positions of these plates and lugs sliding into them must be checked to make sure that the weight is being shared equally among them. It is also important that the door when lowered and shut is well clear of the ground so that no weight is being taken on the bottom edge.

Another type of door is one which is fairly light, flexible and centrally hinged and which, by means of clamps provided at intervals round the edges, makes a tight face joint between the door and the gasket on the door frame. It can be constructed of aluminium channel sections and wooden rails and faced with thin aluminium sheets, the space between them being filled with a light firm insulating material. The inner face of the door does not require painting if it is of high purity aluminium.

With the small access doors provided in well-designed kilns for the easy inspection of instrument bulbs, the operator should ensure that they can always be readily opened from the inside and so eliminate the possibility, though a remote one, of anyone being shut in the kiln.

Bogies
Kiln bogies are very subject to corrosion and should therefore be kept well painted. The bearings should be greased at regular intervals and the rails kept clear and as clean as possible to ensure smooth running of the bogies. Similar servicing of the transfer car and track should also be carried out from time to time and steps taken to keep the track clear of ice in winter.

8.6 Kiln Testing

It is not usually necessary for an operator to make special tests of the effectiveness of a newly installed kiln unless some unusual features or novel devices have been incorporated. It sometimes happens, however, that faults develop with time as, for example, when the doors become worn and inadvertent air leakage occurs, leading to cool moist conditions at one end of the timber pile (see Table on pages 56–57). Such faults are generally made apparent to the observant operator by the behaviour of the timber that he is drying. When, for instance, unusual slowness or lack of uniformity in drying occurs, it is desirable that an operator should know how to carry out a few simple tests to discover the cause, with the object of improving the overall efficiency of his kiln.

1 Temperature and humidity conditions

Temperature and humidity differences along the length of the kiln may be caused by air leakages around the main doors or by the fact that these doors happen to be exposed unduly to north or east winds and are less well insulated than other parts of the building. Frequently the differences along the length are accentuated when a warm control room is situated at the back end of the kiln or a cluster of hot steam-feed pipes are situated within the kiln at that end.

In such circumstances, an obvious method of testing is to introduce wet- and dry-bulb thermometers at various points along the length of the passages or side ducts within the kiln in the path of the circulating air. By taking more or less simultaneous readings of these thermometers it will be possible to detect any really serious differences in the air conditions along the kiln length.

If the differences are particularly marked near the ends of the pile, it is probable that the causes are those already referred to, in which case the necessary remedial action can be taken. It should be possible to improve the insulation and the general fit of the doors, but if this proves to be insufficient to overcome the trouble, an 'end warming' or 'booster' coil can be fitted on the end wall above the door opening in an overhead fan type of kiln, to provide slight additional heat at that end. As this coil will have to be controlled to ensure that just the right amount of heat is added, an indicating instrument such as a dial thermometer should be provided.

Exposed feed pipes at the other end should be lagged and, in exceptional circumstances, it may even be found necessary to rearrange and improve the general heating system. Other possible causes need to be considered and investigated, such as a leak in a steam coil producing a localised zone of high humidity, or a partly blocked steam-spray leading to humidity variations along the length of the kiln.

2 Air circulation tests

When the drying rates of various parts of a kiln load are found to differ markedly and yet no appreciable differences in temperature and humidity can be detected, it is most probable that there is considerable variation in the air speeds through the pile from one part to another.

In an overhead fan kiln, for example, in which the fans are too small or are running too slowly, perhaps due to belt-slip, it may well be that the lower layers of the pile are more or less starved of air. As a result the drying rate of the top part of the pile would always tend to exceed that of the lower.

When an operator has reason to believe that the drying in any kiln is not as rapid or as uniform as it should be, he should first check the temperature and humidity conditions, and if necessary carry out a test on the general air circulation. There are two methods of doing this.

For the first, some means of producing artificial smoke is required. An apparatus can be made in which fumes of hydrochloric acid ('spirits of salt') are blown over ammonium hydroxide, forming a dense white cloud of harmless ammonium chloride particles. A simpler device is obtainable, however, in the form of tubes containing granules of a chemical which produce smoke when damp air is blown through them.

With the aid of a smoke apparatus the operator can study the general movement of air in the kiln by blowing clouds of smoke into the various parts of the air passage. He can see whether there are any sluggish or stagnant zones or parts of the pile into which no air is passing. It is also possible by timing with a stopwatch the passage of a puff of smoke through the known width of stack to obtain quite a close approximation to the actual air speed. Two observers are needed to do this unless the operator arranges a long length of tubing passing to the inlet face of the stack whilst he stands in the outlet side passage and both blows the smoke puff and times it.

In the second method of checking the air circulation, use is made of instruments which give direct readings of the air velocity in any particular spot. One such instrument is the velometer shown in Plate 24a, and another is the hot-wire type of anemometer shown in Plate 24b. The instruments are rather costly and their purchase is probably justified only in the case of kiln manufacturers needing to test the air flow in new designs of kilns and in new plants in which air speeds have been specified by the purchasers. The normal requirements in this respect are dealt with in section 5.2.1.

As already explained in 2.1.1.3, the air speed varies across the depth of the air gap between two layers of wood and it should be noted that the speed, as measured by the smoke-timing method or by a probe type anemometer held in the middle of the gap, is the maximum speed. It cannot, therefore, give an accurate measure of the volume of air passing through the gap. This maximum speed has, however, become the standard basis for the specification of air flow through timber piles.

It will be realised that the ratio of timber thickness to stick thickness (ie depth of air gap) affects the average air speed appreciably. It is unfortunate that for a given stick thickness, the thinner the timber and therefore the faster the drying, the lower is the air speed and hence volume of air to carry the moisture away. The use of variable speed fans appears desirable but is very seldom adopted, chiefly because of the higher initial cost.

Chapter 9 The kiln drying of a load of timber

9.1 Preparation of the load for kiln drying

Before proceeding to desribe in detail the piling and sampling of a kiln load the point must be made that it is highly desirable that the kiln manager or operator should be in overall control of these important activities. However good the kilns may be, the success of drying operations often depends to quite a large extent on the proper preparation of the kiln loads.

1 Piling

The importance of correct, careful piling of timber for kiln drying can scarcely be over-emphasised, particularly if the timber is of a species which is very liable to distort.

Before beginning to pile a kiln load, it is most important to make sure that the foundation of cross bearers on the kiln floor or bogie is firm, strong and absolutely level. An irregular base may well permanently distort several rows of timber at the bottom of a stack, or even the whole pile if the material is thin.

The usual method of piling is to arrange the boards in horizontal layers one above the other, separated by a series of cross piling sticks. These sticks should, if possible, be made of dry, straight-grained timber reasonably free from resin or other substances that might stain the boards. Piling sticks are best made from softwoods or such hardwoods as do not tend to distort much in normal kiln conditions. Sticks 25 × 25 mm in cross-section (1 × 1 in) have proved to be a suitable standard size for general drying but it has been found that 22 × 22 mm ($\frac{7}{8}$ × $\frac{7}{8}$ in) sticks are also quite satisfactory, in kilns with moderate to fast air circulation. When stacking material less than 25 mm (1 in) thick, however, 19 mm ($\frac{3}{4}$ in) sticks may be used in order to keep up the volume of timber accommodated in the kiln. The sticks should be either 19 mm square or 28 × 19 mm so that it is obvious which way they should be laid, for variation in the thickness of sticks in any one layer may easily cause distortion in thin boards.

It might be found in certain circumstances that the kiln output could be increased by using 13 mm ($\frac{1}{2}$ in) sticks, eg in the drying of partly dried or thin refractory hardwoods, but the gain is likely to be offset by the increased breakage losses of such thin pieces. If two different sizes of stick are used in the one battery of kilns, precautions must obviously be taken to ensure that they do not get mixed. In the majority of plants, however, it will be found better to employ one standard size of stick, this being dictated largely by the thickness of timber most often dried. Sticks should be kept as clean and dry as possible and of course handled with reasonable care to minimise wastage.

Each vertical line of sticks should be fully supported by a bearer on the floor of the kiln or on the kiln trolley. *Plate 25*. Those at each end of the stack should be as near the end as possible and the spacing between the main rows of sticks should be varied according to the timber that is to be dried. Most softwoods and those hardwoods which show little tendency to distort when in thicknesses of 50 mm (2 in) and upwards may be piled with the vertical rows of sticks spaced at intervals of 900 mm (3 ft) maximum, but for thinner boards it is advisable to reduce the space to 600 mm (2 ft). Those softwoods and hardwoods which tend to distort appreciably during drying should have sticks at intervals of not more than 600 mm (2 ft). Boards of these species 25 mm (1 in) or less in thickness are best stacked with the sticks spaced no more than 450 mm (18 in) apart. For elm and any timber in which the quality or grain of the wood is such as to render the timber particularly prone to various forms of distortion, spacings no wider than 300 mm (12 in) are strongly to be recommended. In all cases care should be taken to place the sticks, as piling proceeds, in absolute vertical alignment, so that the weight of the stack is directly transmitted through the lines of sticks to the bearers on the floor or kiln bogie. Distortion of timber in seasoning may be considerably reduced by a proper arrangement of the piling sticks but mis-alignment tends only to aggravate such degrade.

A satisfactory standard of piling can best be obtained by adopting a definite routine. On the completion of each layer of timber the sticks should be correctly placed across it. A few of them are liable to be displaced, however, when the first board or plank is laid on them, and so immediately after this these sticks should be readjusted into their correct positions. If left until later there may be too much weight on the sticks for this to be done properly, even by two men, and hammering the ends so that they are in alignment is not very effective. The latter is little more than window-dressing and often results in the sticks being curved or broken.

Some kiln supervisors have found it worthwhile to use piling guides to ensure that the sticks are placed in vertical alignment and that the vertical sides of a pile are kept even. Such guides consist of a simple framework of battens or of light metal channel supported vertically against the kiln bogie and providing grooves into which the piling sticks can be pushed. *Plate 26*.

When heavy planks have to be piled with limited labour and without the help of a crane, and when the pile rises above shoulder height, the work can be eased by lifting each plank up on to one end of the stack and using rollers (eg short lengths of 50 mm steam pipe) to manœuvre it into position. In this case it is advisable to get the first plank in each layer into position by pushing it on rollers over the completed layer beneath it and then introducing the piling sticks under it.

When a variety of lengths has to be piled and it is not possible to combine various lengths to make up the full length of the bogie, it is convenient to place the longest boards at the bottom and to reduce the length of the pile as the height increases, keeping one of the ends flush. Alternatively, if sorting of lengths is not practicable or not economic, which is often the case, a pile of uniform length may be built by arranging the boards as shown in Figure 7.

The ends of boards, especially of thin material, are liable to distort badly if unsupported, and when it is absolutely impossible to avoid introducing a number of long boards which overhang the ends of the stack, special supports for these should be erected. It should be mentioned, however, that the use of supports does not represent an ideal solution and is only the lesser of two evils since, as the load dries and shrinks, the level of the stack falls, whilst the height of the supports remains relatively unchanged and so induces a slight upward sweep at the ends of the projecting boards resting on them. Within the pile itself, short lengths of sticks should be inserted both under and over the ends of those boards which do not quite reach the vertical lines of piling sticks.

For the drying of any timber which is known to be particularly prone to distort, it is recommended that the top of each bogie load should be weighted down with concrete slabs or other suitable non-ferrous material as this will minimise the amount of degrade in the otherwise unrestrained top rows.

The width and height of pile in a kiln will naturally be chiefly dependent upon the cross-sectional dimension of the kiln and on the quantity of timber to be dried. The width of the air passages between the pile and the side walls should be such as is recommended by the designer to give uniformity of air flow. On no account should the load encroach much on the air inlet passage in order to accommodate more timber for this may adversely affect the air circulation through the pile.

In all types of kiln in which the circulating air enters the inlet side passage vertically, the sides of the pile should be made as even as possible with no boards projecting appreciably beyond the others. Boards which jut out appreciably will tend to act as deflectors causing an excess of air to pass through one or two spaces at the expense of others, as illustrated in Figure 19.

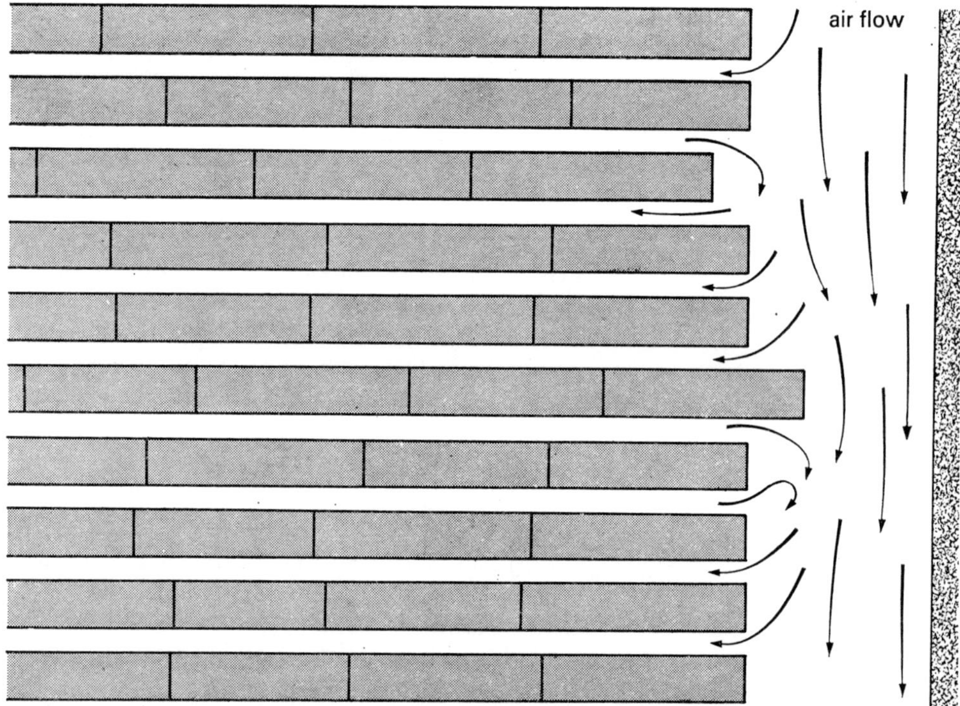

Figure 19 *Effect of irregular pile face on air circulation*

It is an advantage of the side fan kilns with horizontal air flow, that an irregular-faced pile has no adverse effect on the circulation. Obviously, however, pieces jutting out overmuch may foul the door frame when the load is run into the kiln and volume is lost if many layers are much below the full width.

Two other points should be noted in the stacking of loads for horizontal flow kilns. The gaps between the face of the stack and the end wings of the fan boxes should be as small as possible or should be blanked off to prevent excessive short-circuiting. Secondly, the piling should be so arranged that there is a vertical tier opposite each wing to ensure that air entering into the stack there must traverse the full width before re-entering and being pulled back into the fan. These effects are illustrated in A and B respectively in Figure 20.

Whenever possible, different species and thicknesses should be piled separately and not mixed in any one kiln load. In a mixed load the thick or refractory timber will dry more slowly than the other material in the pile, with the result that either the former is insufficiently dried or the latter tends to become overdried. Where mixing is absolutely unavoidable the kiln treatment has to be based on the behaviour of the least tolerant material and it is advisable to pile the faster drying timber on the upper part of the stack. By so doing it becomes possible to remove it before it becomes overdried, without, at the same time, disturbing the remainder. Even so, the relatively mild conditions to which this more tolerant material is subjected resulted in the drying time being longer than if it were dried separately to the appropriate schedule.

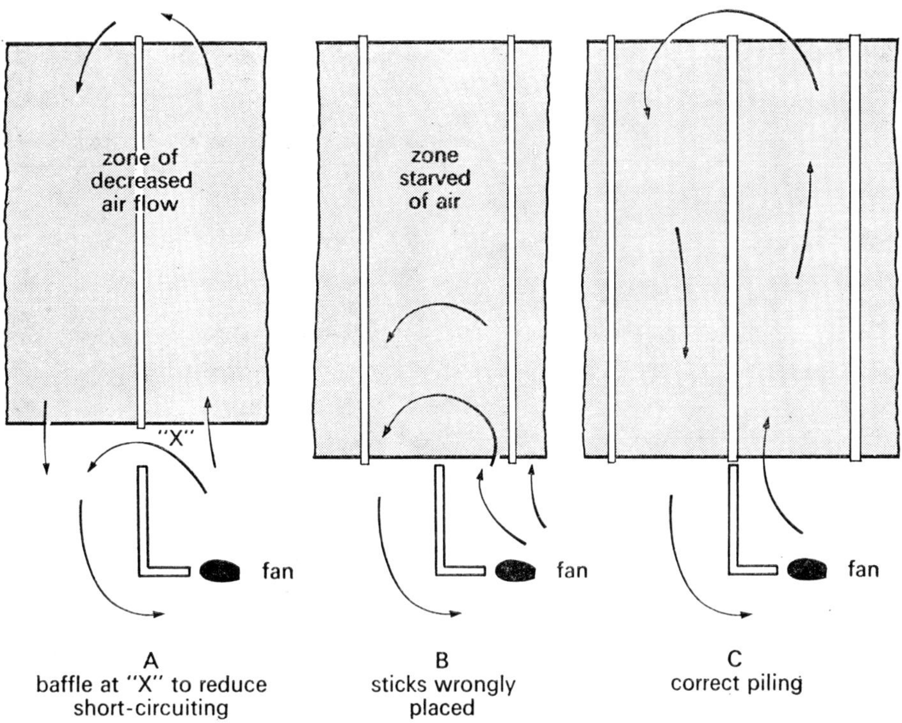

Figure 20 *Piling of timber in side fan horizontal flow kilns*

In all forced-circulation kilns it is recommended that the boards or planks in each layer should be placed edge to edge. An exception should be made, however, when drying squares or scantlings more than about 65 mm ($2\frac{1}{2}$ in) thick, for then advantage can be taken of some drying from the side faces if gaps of about 10 mm ($\frac{3}{8}$ in) are left between each piece in a layer.

In any kiln the circulating air will always have a tendency to by-pass the timber through spaces inadvertently formed above, below or along the stack. It is recommended that this short-circuiting should be minimised by sealing off such spaces by means of canvas curtains or baffles made of wood or other suitable material. Occasionally a load of timber may have to be dried which will only partly fill the particular kiln available. In such cases it is usually advantageous to reduce the width of stack sufficiently to bring the pile to approximately normal height.

Certain timber items cut to standard sizes can conveniently be piled without the use of a large number of sticks. For instance, small furniture parts such as chair leg squares, rails etc, can be self-crossed in the manner shown in Figure 21.

Here the pieces themselves are so small that they can be used in place of the normal piling sticks without fear of restricting the air flow unduly. In order that the individual stacks so formed in making up the complete load should be reasonably stable and not tend to topple over when shrinkage occurs, sticks should be introduced at intervals across the full width of the stack to act as tie-rods. A method of piling small but relatively wide pieces of timber, such as brush-back blanks, without much overlapping of the surfaces, is illustrated in Plate 27. In kilns used solely for the drying of small dimension stock, the usual bogies and rails can be dispensed with as the stocks can be piled on pallets which are run into the kiln on small lift trucks.

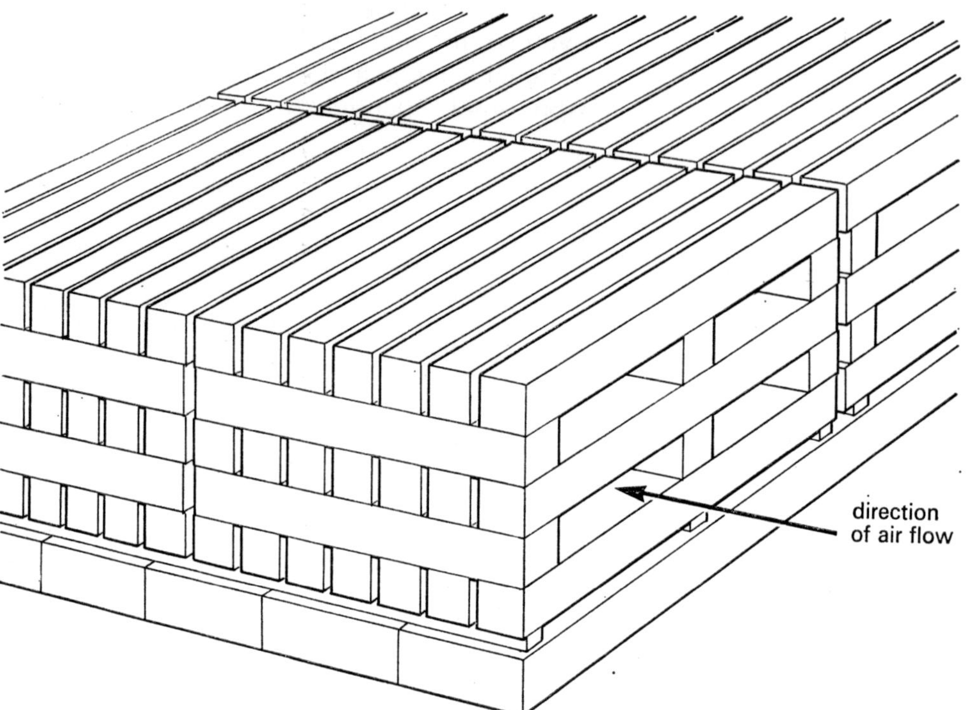

Figure 21 *Cross-piling of dimension stock*

2 Mechanical aids to piling and handling of loads

The cost of the handling of timber constitutes quite a large part of the total cost of kiln drying, particularly in the case of material which only requires a short time in the kilns. A number of aids to piling are available and the size of the kiln installation and the type of timber being dried dictate which of them is both practical and the most economical.

At plants where neither a fork lift nor a side loader is on hand, and in which heavy boards or planks have to be piled, a small mobile crane or a travelling gantry can be most useful. When mechanical trucks are available they can be used in a number of ways. They can be used to dump packs of timber on trestles of convenient heights placed alongside the stacks as loading proceeds. In larger plants which can bear the cost of some extra equipment, the timber can be deposited alongside the stack, on scissor lift platforms which are progressively raised to keep level with the layer being piled. *Plate 28*.

The method most commonly adopted when the material being dried is of a reasonably uniform length and not too wide, is that of building packages or setts approximately 900 mm (3 ft) to 1200 mm (4 ft) wide and of similar height and fork-lifting these on top of one another and side by side to build up the full kiln load. The setts can either be deposited on bogies and then run into the kiln in the usual manner *Plate 29*, or built up directly on the kiln floor in kilns designed with full length side doors for this purpose.

A disadvantage of the use of fork lifts, though not a major one, is the tendency for piling sticks to become displaced during transport, especially when the setts are of thin boards. This can be reduced by introducing extra sticks in the bottom two or three layers roughly above the points of contact of the forks.

The mechanical aid which can effect a great improvement in both the rate and standard of piling is the lumber lift which, by lowering the stack into a pit as it is being built, keeps the top always at the most convenient height for putting on the next layer. *Plate 30*. Lumber lifts, which involve considerable excavation, are costly to install and may only be justified in large plants with quick drying loads or when the cheaper alternative of building up setts is not practicable.

In North America and Scandinavia where there are kiln plants drying vast numbers of fairly uniform size pieces, fully automatic stackers have been developed and used with advantage. Similar but smaller equipment has been introduced in Germany, but it is doubtful whether in the UK there are any firms which would find the installation of the apparatus an economic proposition.

Automatic unloading by a tilting and lifting of the setts is practicable in some cases and has been used in this country. The boards or planks slide on to a conveyor leading them to cross-cut saws and planing machines whilst the sticks are segregated and conveyed back to the stacking area.

Installations consisting of more than 2 or 3 kilns should be laid out with a transfer track across the front of the kilns and loading and unloading bays as illustrated in Plate 15. Normally bogie loads can be manhandled on to the transfer car along the track and in and out of the kilns, sometimes with the judicious aid of any powered vehicle available. In very large plants, however, it is found economic to invest in a purpose-built, power driven transfer car complete with a capstan for moving loads in and out of the kilns. *Plate 31*.

9.2 Kiln samples

Need for samples

Some means of determining the current state of dryness of a kiln load is nearly always required.

Most schedules of kiln treatment are based on the moisture content of the timber as it dries. Exceptions arise when previous experience with any particular species and size of known initial moisture content enables the operator to prescribe combinations of temperatures and humidities on a time basis.

Weighing of the whole load, if practicable, would indicate the average drying rate but could give no idea of the considerable variation in moisture content which develops because of inherent differences in the drying properties of individual pieces or in drying conditions from one part of a stack to another.

By embedding electrical contacts in a number of pieces in the kiln stack and taking leads from them to a moisture meter outside the kiln, approximate values of the moisture content of these pieces can be obtained. Readings of over approximately 30 per cent moisture content are subject to considerable error and corrections for temperature have to be made. This method is used in one of the fully automatic control systems described under 6.5.

The most widely adopted method of gauging the progress of drying consists of having a number of prepared sample pieces which can be withdrawn from the stack and weighed to estimate their moisture content. By their use (a) schedules based on moisture content, whether the average or that of the wettest sample can be followed, (b) the variation likely to exist from piece to piece in the load is indicated and (c) in the course of weighing the samples, examination of any checking or excessive distortion developing will reveal whether any modifications in the kiln treatment are called for. Tests for moisture distribution across the section and for casehardening can readily be made on the samples as required. Removable samples can be used for ascertaining the uniformity of drying conditions throughout a kiln. Where the material being dried permits the use of time schedules, kiln samples are essential in the initial development of such schedules.

The chief disadvantages of the method lie in the time involved in the preparation, incorporation in the stack and periodic withdrawal and weighing of the samples, and in the small loss of timber used for them. In general, however, the advantages of the removable sample method are held to outweigh the disadvantages, and guidance as to the selection, number, size, preparation and positioning of kiln samples follows.

1 Number and selection of samples
Obviously the kiln samples should be as representative as possible of the load being dried and the proper selection of them as the timber is being stacked is an important part of the operator's responsibilities.

Many variables in the drying behaviour of the timber in the kiln have to be considered. In the desirable case of a load in which all the material is of one species and thickness, the main factors applying are (a) the initial moisture content, particularly with softwoods in which the sapwood is usually much wetter than the heartwood (b) the way in which each piece was sawn on conversion; quarter-sawn boards nearly always dry more slowly than do plain-sawn ones and only the latter are prone to surface check on the face (c) except in very fast air speed kilns, the difference in drying rate across the width of the stack.

Ideally, in a load of boards or planks sawn through and through, six samples should be taken and of these, two should be quarter-sawn pieces and two plain-sawn. An attempt should be made to include one or two of the wettest and of the driest pieces being piled. The wetter of the quarter-sawn samples placed in the slowest drying position (see 9.2.4) and the wetter of the plain-sawn ones on the air-inlet side of the stack will give an indication of the extremes of drying rate that occur. The wetter plain-sawn piece on the inlet side will represent the material most likely to surface check. In order to avoid overdrying, and hence extra distortion, it is necessary to know the lowest moisture content reached at any time and this will be shown by placing the driest plain or near plain-sawn piece on an air inlet side of the stack.

The number of samples may be reduced to three or four when an operator is drying a load of timber known to be of a fairly uniform moisture content and of a species with which he has had much experience. On the other hand, when there is unavoidable mixing of different species and/or different thicknesses in any one load, the number of samples needed to give a truly representative picture of the progress of drying is increased. The slowest drying material and the most refractory species (which will dictate the kiln treatment given) must be sampled and also the fastest drying stock (so that it is known when to withdraw this if possible or to apply a conditioning treatment 7.2.3). The total number of samples taken will depend to a large extent on the precision in final moisture content required but is bound also to be limited to what is practicable and economic.

2 Size of samples
The size of kiln samples to be taken will depend in the first place on the dimensions of the timber being dried. When handling long stock the samples should not be less than about 1500 mm (5 ft) long and the ends should be coated with a moisture resistant preparation, such as

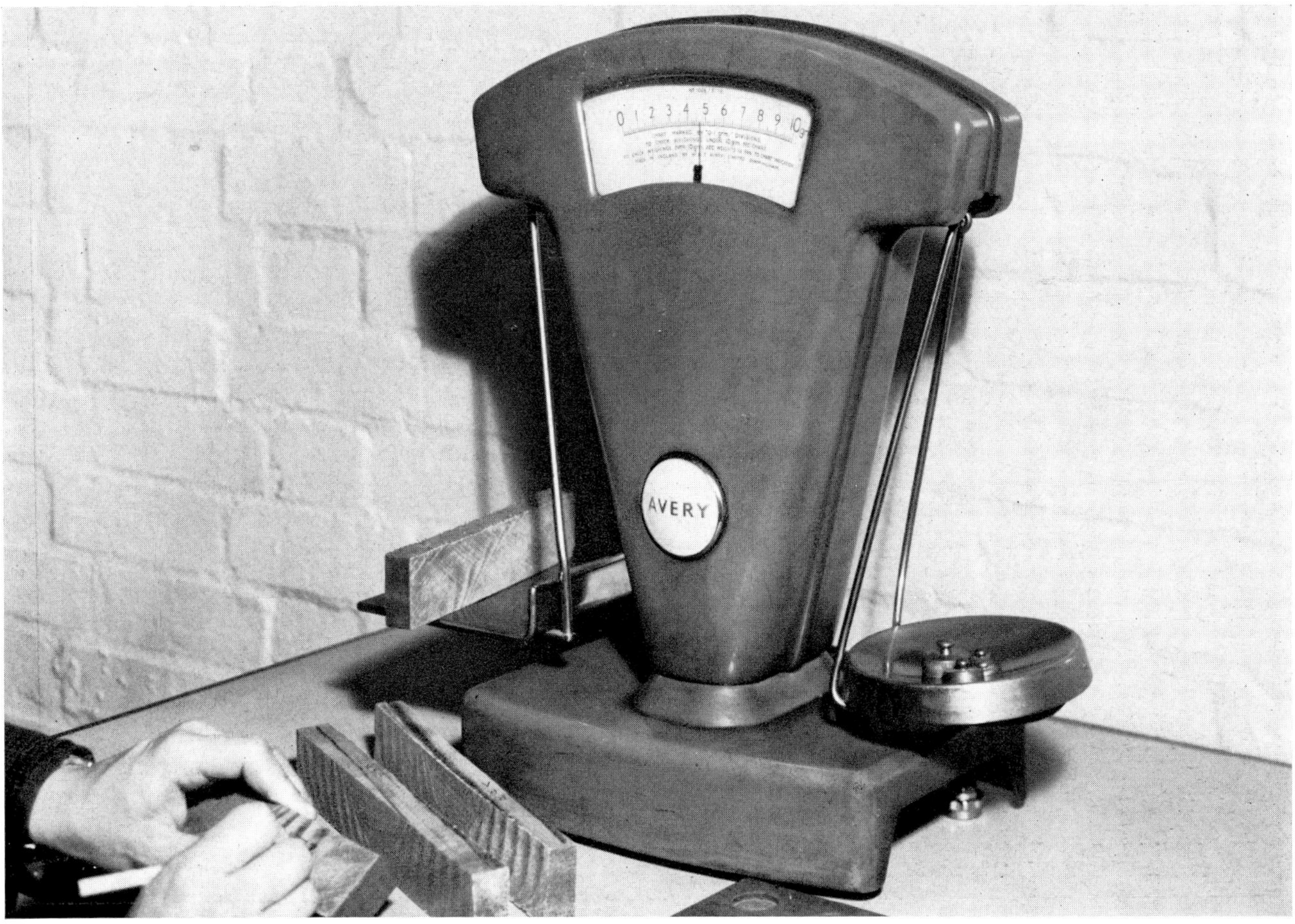

Plate 1 *Semi-automatic balance for weighing moisture content test pieces*

Plate 2 *Ventilated drying oven*

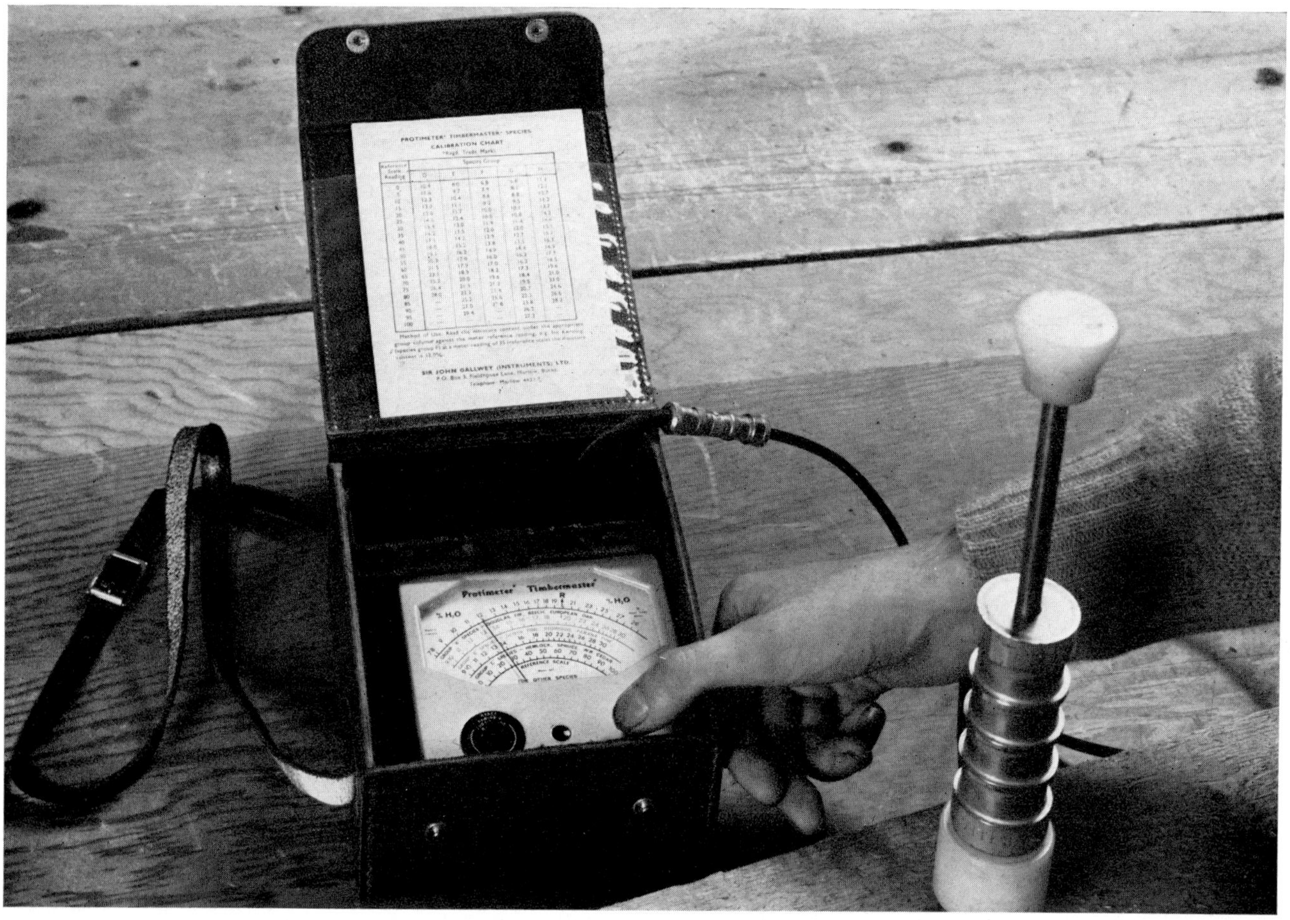

Plate 3 *Moisture meter and hammer-type electrodes*

Plate 4 *Forced air drying trials at Princes Risborough*

Plate 5 *Dehumidifiers in a forced draught timber drier*

Plate 6 *Plank of oak showing surface checking, end splitting and end checking*

Plate 7 *Honeycombing in yellow seraya*

Plate 8 *Collapsed (top) and reconditioned (bottom) board of Tasmanian oak*

Plate 9 *Stick stain in planed board of beech*

Plate 10 *Air drying of poles*

Plate 11 *Beech piled in log form in a well kept air seasoning yard*

Plate 12 *Fans, gilled steam heating pipes, spray and vents in an overhead cross shaft fan kiln—above the false ceiling*

Plate 13 *Fan, oil-fired heat exchanger and disc-type humidifier in a side fan kiln*

Plate 14 *Fans and steam heating pipes in a side fan kiln*

Plate 15 *Battery of prefabricated metal side fan kilns*

Plate 16 *Kiln sample on semi-automatic scales*

Plate 17A *A wet- and dry-bulb temperature recorder*

Plate 17B *Wet- and dry-bulb thermometer bulbs with water trough for wet-bulb fabric covering fed from larger reservoir or drip-feed outside kiln*

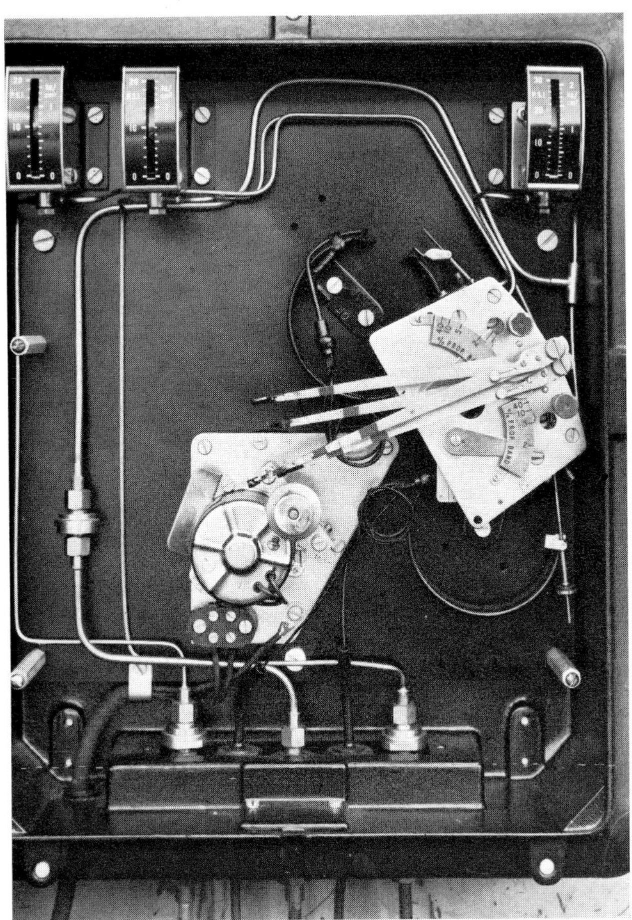

Plate 18 *Interior of an air-operated wet- and dry-bulb temperature recorder/controller giving proportional control*

Plate 19 *Interior of an electrically operated recorder/controller*

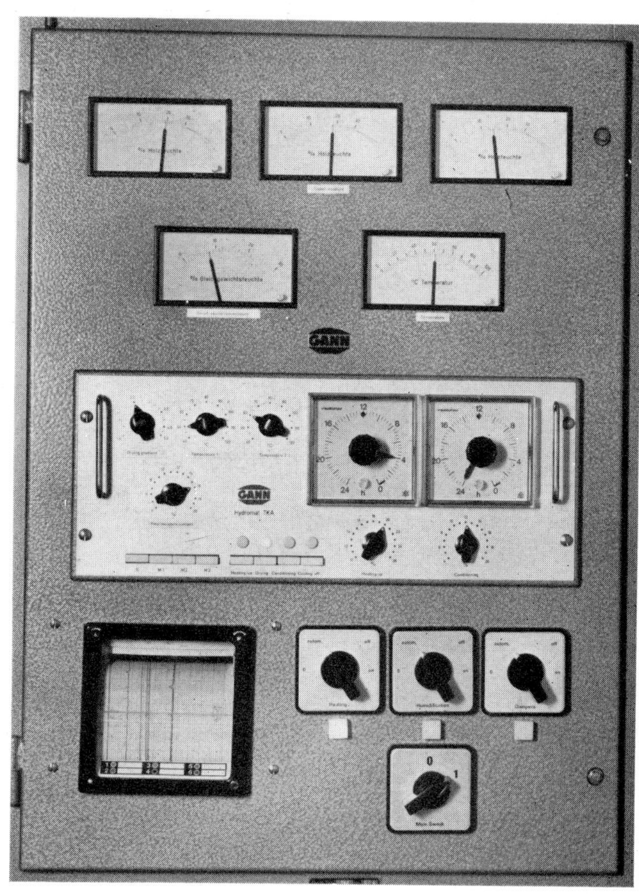

Plate 20 *Gann Hydromat Control Panel*

Plate 21 *Gann kiln controller—Meter leads and wafer of wood monitoring EMC in kiln air*

Plate 22 *Well-kept operating room*

Plate 23 *Aluminium carrier door*

Plate 24A *Instruments for measuring air velocity—Velometer*

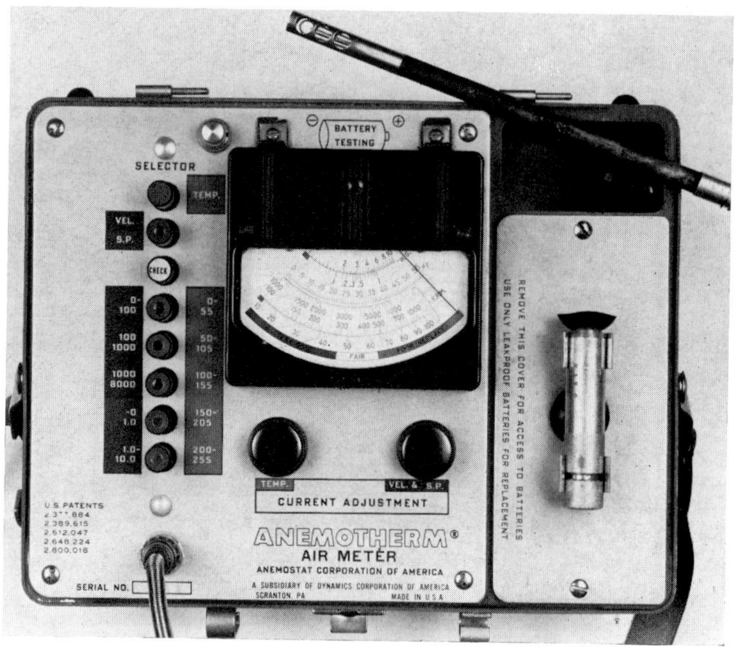

Plate 24B *Instruments for measuring air velocity—Hot wire type anemometer*

Plate 25 *A well piled kiln load*

Plate 26 *A piling stick guide*

Plate 27 *End lapping of small boards*

Plate 28 *Scissor lift platform (at full height)*

Plate 29 *Fork lift loading sett on to kiln bogie*

Plate 30 *Piling stack on a lumber lift*

Plate 31 *Power-driven transfer car*

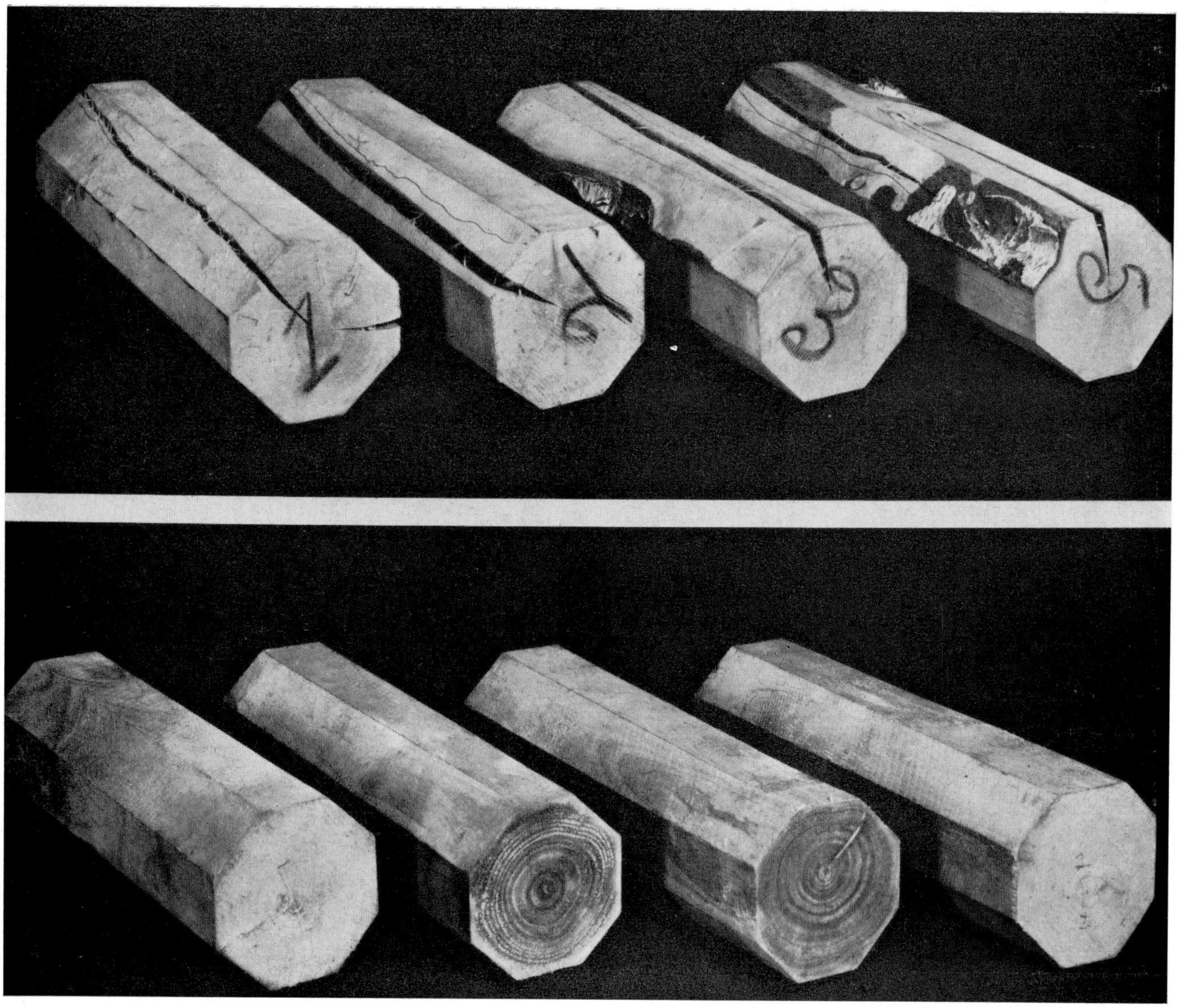

Plate 32 *Birch billets after drying a (top) untreated b (bottom) urea-treated*

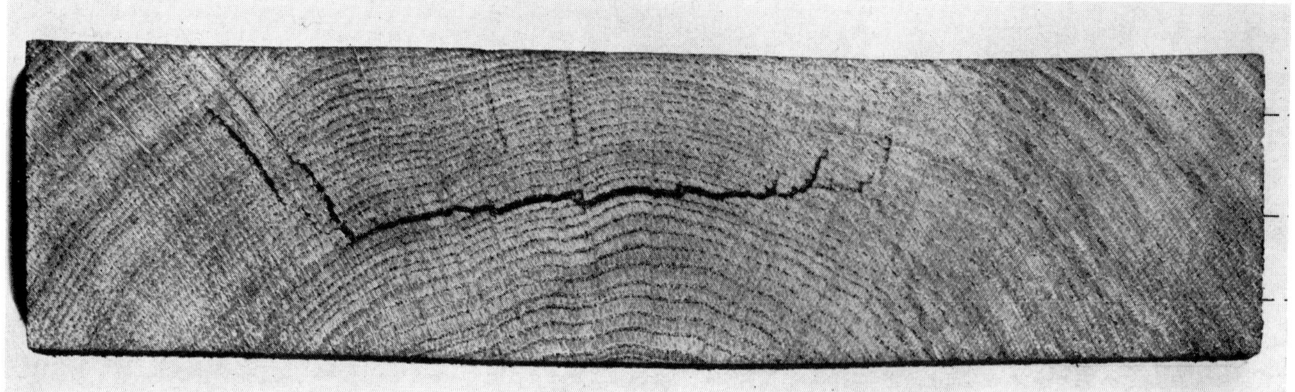

Plate 33 *'Bursting' in English oak dried by RF heating*

thick bituminous paint, to prevent disproportionate loss of moisture through the end-grain.

Somewhat shorter samples may sometimes be taken owing to practical difficulties in accommodating long ones or because in thick, heavy material, fuller length pieces would be too unwieldy to handle and possibly too heavy for the scales available. Cost is another consideration, for example when drying valuable timber such as rosewood or teak. When using short samples in such cases it is of paramount importance that their ends be really well sealed. Samples should be of similar widths to those of the timber in the kiln load but in the case of very wide boards and planks they may for convenience be cut to about 230 mm (9 in) wide.

3 Preparation and use of samples

The kiln samples are prepared from the piece selected by cross cutting and taking moisture test sections in the manner described in 1.4.2. As soon as possible after cutting, the samples should be weighed on suitable scales and their ends sealed with moisture resistant paint. Ordinary counter scales and sets of decimal weights are adequate for the weighing of kiln samples, but when there are large numbers of them to be weighed daily a semi-automatic weighing machine is a worthwhile investment. *Plate 16*.

By assuming that the moisture content of the sample is the same as that of the small test piece cut from it, the estimated dry weight of the whole sample can be calculated. It is then possible simply by weighing the sample to estimate its moisture content at any subsequent time without having to re-cut it.

Suppose that the initial average moisture content, as determined by the oven drying method, was 35 per cent and that at the same time the sample board weighed 12.40 kg; then the dry weight of the board would be:

$$\frac{\text{Wet weight}}{(\text{mc}/100 + 1)} = \frac{12{\cdot}40}{1{\cdot}35} = 9{\cdot}18 \text{ kg}$$

This estimated dry weight remains a constant quantity as long as no further wood is cut from the board.

Suppose that after a period of drying, the weight of this sample falls to 11·72 kg, the moisture content would be:

$$\left(\frac{\text{Current Weight}}{\text{Dry weight}} - 1\right) \times 100 = \left(\frac{11{\cdot}72}{9{\cdot}18} - 1\right) \times 100 = 27{\cdot}6 \text{ per cent}$$

It must be fully realised that this is an estimated moisture content based on the assumption that the test piece initially gave the true average of the whole, whereas in practice, the fact that the moisture is seldom uniformly distributed along the length of a board may lead to errors that become significant when the desired final moisture content is approached. Even when, as is ideal, a moisture test is made at each end of a sample and the moisture content is taken as being the average of the two, an appreciable error can occur.

It is always advisable, therefore, some time before the conclusion of a kiln run, to determine afresh the moisture content of a board by the cutting and oven drying of test samples. At the same time it is often a good plan to discover the manner in which the moisture is distributed through the section of the kiln sample, particularly if the material is likely to be re-sawn or heavily machined.

For this purpose, when the moisture content determination is made on the timber, an additional cross-section is cut from it and sub-divided by sawing into strips in the manner indicated in Figure 22. The outer edges are removed from the inner strips and all the strips are then weighed separately, dried in an oven and re-weighed so that the moisture content of each can be calculated.

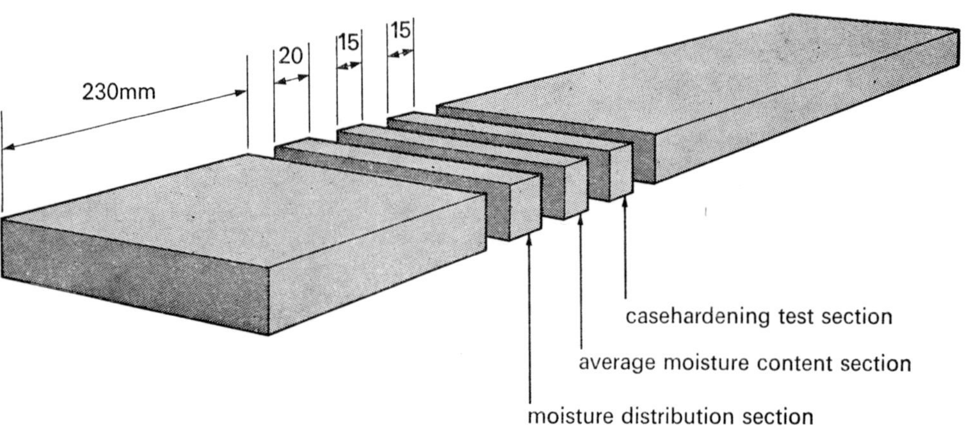

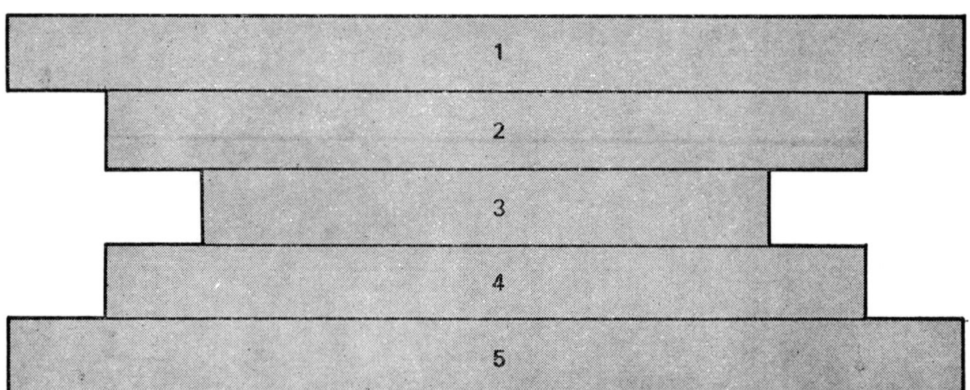

Figure 22 *Re-cutting of kiln sample for testing moisture content, average and distribution; also casehardening (see Fig 5)*

It is often desirable also at this time to carry out casehardening tests by cutting sections and prongs as described in section 3.4.

After a sample board has been cut for re-estimation of moisture content and other tests it must be re-weighed so that its new dry weight can be calculated.

There are certain species whose average moisture content is difficult to determine by normal sampling methods. Poplar, teak, hemlock and western red cedar, for example, are liable to vary considerably along the length, retaining local pockets of moisture, so that the re-estimated moisture contents may differ very appreciably from the values estimated from the initial cutting. If, on occasion, it is essential to dry a load of such a species to a very uniform moisture content throughout, the need for taking more samples than usual and for thorough final re-estimation is obvious and the kiln run will take longer than is normal.

When dealing with short dimension stock a slightly different method of preparing samples has to be adopted. Samples of truly representative size and known moisture content can be obtained by cutting the test section from the middle of, say, a short furniture square, painting the fresh cut ends and joining the two halves tightly together with corrugated fasteners. Such a method cannot be used, however, when drying still smaller items such as flooring blocks, brush backs or bobbins. In these cases a number of pieces should be oven dried initially to ascertain the general average moisture content of the kiln load. Other marked samples may be withdrawn for weighing from time to time in order to study roughly the progress of drying and later in the run moisture tests can, if practicable, be made on them with a meter, provided they have been allowed to cool first. When the desired moisture content is apparently reached, further check tests by oven drying should be made on these and other pieces taken from various parts of the stack, trays, or racks, as the case may be.

4 Positioning of samples

The samples should be so placed that they will indicate the drying rate and behaviour of the wood, (a) in the fastest drying part of the stack, ie on the side where the circulating air enters it and (b) in the slowest drying part. In kilns in which the circulation is reversed at regular intervals the slowest drying part is halfway along the air path through the stack. Although in many kilns it is more difficult to arrange for the easy withdrawal of samples from this second position, it is obviously very desirable to obtain some indication of the moisture contents there. The sampling of the middle of the stack is particularly important in some of the older kilns with wide stacks and rather slow air circulation. The middle samples need not be weighed until those on the inlet sides are nearing the desired final moisture content.

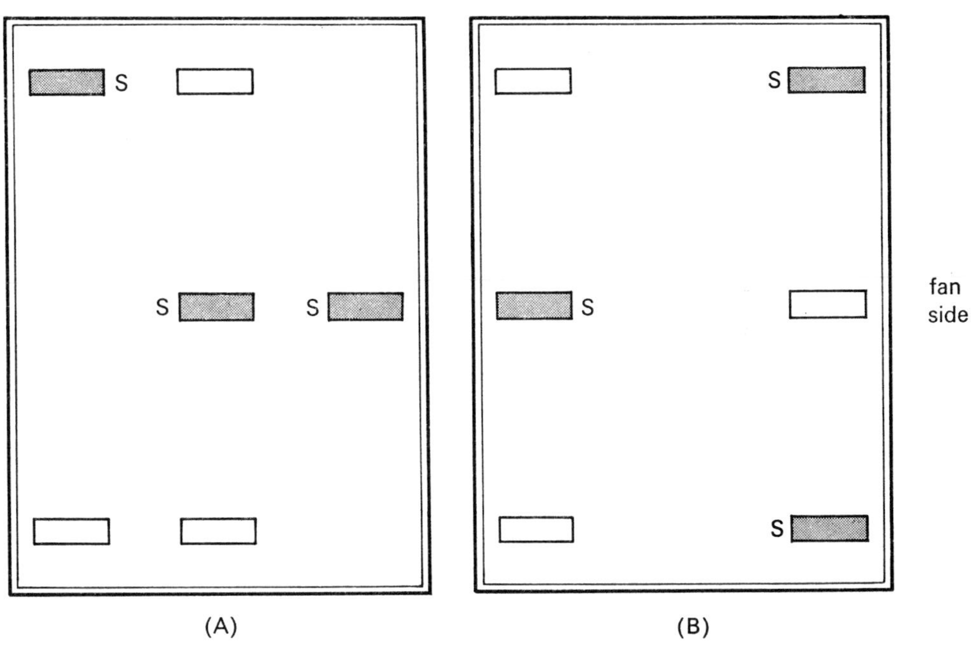

Figure 23 *Distribution of samples in the load in a kiln (A) with overhead fans (B) with side fans and horizontal flow*

In kilns of the side fan horizontal air flow type with frequent reversal, the slowest drying portion of the stack is on the side remote from the fan/s. A simple and suitable arrangement of six samples in the two cases cited is shown in Figure 23. In order to identify each sample for weighing and recording purposes and to ensure its replacement in the correct position, some system of lettering or numbering the samples should be adopted.

The method of building samples into the stack must be such that the drying treatment they receive is in every way similar to that of the wood in their vicinity; moreover, it must allow for their relatively easy withdrawal for weighing. It is time wasting for the operator when some of the samples become difficult or impossible to remove or replace, though this, unfortunately, is sometimes unavoidable when the timber is prone to distort badly.

One method of accommodating withdrawable samples is to place sticks over them which have been notched out to about half the thickness of the sticks. This tends to be time consuming and rather wasteful of sticks unless it is feasible to have samples of standard width and position, in which case the notched sticks can be used repeatedly.

An alternative arrangement, using suitable lengths of sticks of half the normal thickness, is shown in Figure 24.

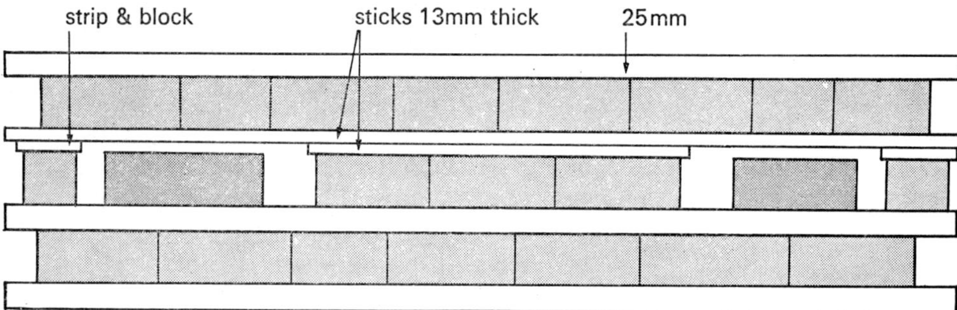

Figure 24 *Method of accommodating withdrawable kiln samples*

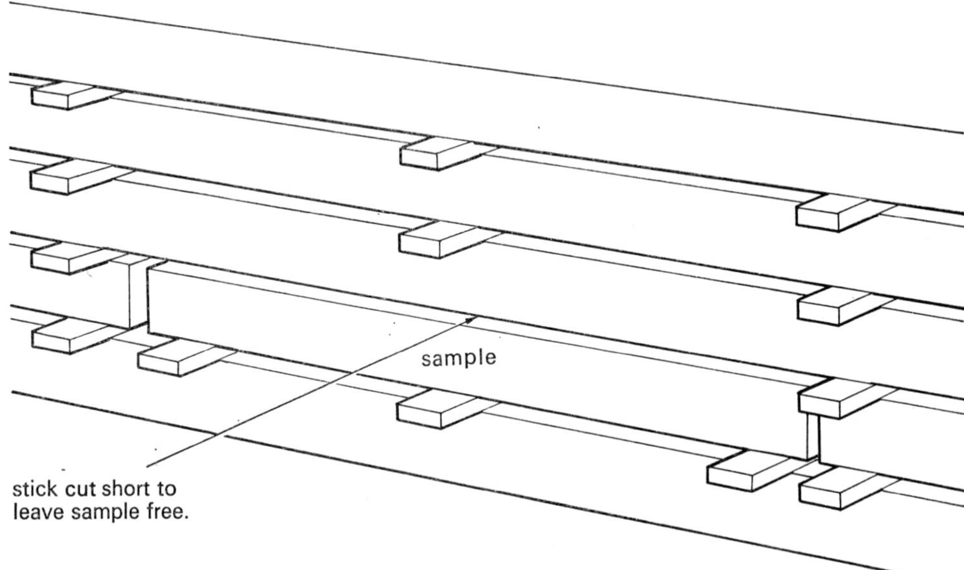

Figure 25 *Method of accommodating sample in the side of a kiln stack*

Both these methods involve opening the large doors for the removal of the samples but the kiln conditions soon return to normal, especially if automatic control is in operation, and there is the advantage that the condition of the load can readily be examined at the time of sample weighing.

Samples can be accommodated in the sides of stacks by cutting a couple of sticks off short as illustrated in Figure 25, thus leaving the sample free. The samples can be removed by entering the kiln through the small access doors instead of the main door. However, because the operator then has to enter a hot, damp kiln he may be discouraged from weighing the samples as often as he should and even from applying an appropriate high temperature schedule. There is also a tendency for him to use samples which are much too short and to put them on projecting ends, eg in spaces between bogie loads, where they will dry abnormally fast.

9.3 Application of kiln treatments

Standard Schedules

Experience has shown that satisfactory kiln drying can usually be best accomplished by gradually raising the temperature and lowering the humidity of the circulating air as drying proceeds. The normal procedure is to gauge the progress of drying by periodic weighing of removable samples, and to make changes to the temperature and humidity of the inlet air when the wettest inlet sample reaches prescribed moisture content levels. The set of temperatures and humidities and the moisture content levels at which changes are to be applied is referred to as a drying 'schedule'. It has already been indicated that the rates at which different timber species can safely be dried, and the air conditions to which they can be subjected without suffering damage, vary very considerably, and the treatment applied should, therefore, depend to a large extent on the species that is being dried. From first hand experience in the kiln drying of a large number of species, and from data obtained elsewhere, the Princes Risborough Laboratory has prepared the list of Schedules, given in Appendix B. There are other factors besides species which determine the most appropriate schedule to be applied to a particular load, but as a compromise, and to avoid undue complication, the Laboratory has grouped the various timbers into twelve categories and recommended a separate schedule for each category. The schedules as given are designed for use with timber of random width, between 25 mm (1 in) and 38 mm ($1\frac{1}{2}$ in) thick and on the assumption that a forced-draught type of kiln, with an average air speed through the stack of 1 to $1\frac{1}{2}$ m/s, will be used for the drying.

In general, these schedules are comparatively mild and can usually be relied upon to give satisfactory results. Kiln operators who have to dry loads with which they have had no previous experience are advised to make use of them as they stand, unless there are special considerations (see below) which make it clear from the start that some modification is necessary or until their own experience indicates that modifications can be made with advantage.

9.4 Modifications to a schedule

1 Before the commencement of a run

Some desirable alterations to the standard schedules given in Appendix B can be prescribed in advance, being based on known features of the kiln used and of the load to be dried.

1.1 Air Speed

The behaviour of any timber during kiln drying is determined by the temperatures to which it is subjected, and on the rates at which moisture is allowed to evaporate from the surfaces. These rates are dependent not only on the humidities of the air entering the stack but also on its speed of movement over the timber. It follows that if the schedule of temperatures and humidities used in a kiln with comparatively slow air circulation is the same as that used in one with a faster flow, the treatment actually received by the timber is milder and the drying rate slower. It is therefore advisable in older kilns in which the air movement is known to be slow (say 0·6 m/sec (2 ft/sec) or less), to lower the recommended humidities by 5 to 10 per cent at each stage and this can be done without increasing the risk that checking may occur. On the other hand, of course, in modern kilns with a very fast air circulation (say 2 to 3 m/sec ($6\frac{1}{2}$ to 10 ft/sec)), application of the standard schedules causes faster drying and involves an increased risk of splitting and checking, and when drying species which are very prone to this type of degrade it would be a sensible precaution to raise the recommended humidities by 5 per cent at each stage.

1.2 Thickness

The thickness of the timber has a bearing on the schedule to be employed in that the greater the thickness, the steeper the moisture gradient is likely to be from surface to centre for a given set of drying conditions. As a consequence, the drying stresses set up will tend to be greater and the tendency to check or to honeycomb will increase. Thick stock should, therefore, be subjected to higher humidity conditions than thin material. For thicknesses between 38 mm (1½ in) and 75 mm (3 in), humidities 5 per cent higher at each stage of the otherwise appropriate schedule should be used, and a 10 per cent increase, at any rate until the final stages of drying, is often desirable with timber greater than 75 mm (3 in) in thickness. On the other hand, with timber less than 25 mm (1 in) thick the humidity can be 5 to 10 per cent lower at each stage, except on species such as oak and greenheart which are particularly susceptible to checking.

1.3 Strength

Where the strength properties of the dried material are of considerable importance, as for example in timbers required for sports goods, vehicle construction or tool handles, the kiln temperature should not exceed about 60°C. Tests have shown that prolonged treatment at higher temperatures can have an adverse effect on the impact strength of the timber.

It has been found that timber which has been impregnated with some types of water-borne fireproofing salts suffers a loss in strength if kiln-dried at high tempratures. It is important, therefore, that such treated timber, if intended for structural use, should be re-dried only at low or moderate temperatures in order to keep strength losses to a minimum.

1.4 Resin Exudation

The resins and gums contained in some species are liable to exude on to the surfaces of the timber if drying is conducted at temperatures much above 50°C. In some instances, this effect is considered beneficial in that the resin removed during drying cannot exude later when the timber is in use, and the timbers are dried at the highest temperatures which in other respects they are able to withstand. In cases where resin exudation must be avoided, however, because it would be deemed to mar the appearance of the timber, the kiln temperature should be limited to 50°C and a slower rate of drying accepted.

1.5 Colour

Many timbers tend to darken in colour when dried at high temperatures and this effect is greatest when high humidities are also employed during the early stages of a run. Where it is particularly important to retain the natural light colour of the wood, as with sycamore and sometimes with beech, the best hope of doing so lies in maintaining a temperature of about 35°C throughout the run and commencing the drying at a humidity 10 to 15 per cent lower than would normally be used, even though this may cause some checking to occur on plain-sawn surfaces. It is also advisable in such cases, in order to avoid wetting the load by condensation, that the initial warming up process should be carried out without using the steam spray.

1.6 Air Dried Timber

In timber which has been partly air dried before it enters the kiln, the moisture content of the surface layers is usually higher, and the moisture gradient from surface to centre less steep, than in similar material which has been brought to the same average moisture content by kiln drying from the green. Moreover, there is always a possibility that some surface checking has already been initiated during the preliminary air drying. Immediate application of the normal schedule to air dried material at the stage appropriate to its average moisture content may therefore cause too rapid surface drying and consequent formation of new checking or the re-opening and extension of existing checks.

For this reason, it is advisable where possible to commence drying at the humidity appropriate to a moisture content at least two stages higher than that of the wettest sample in the load. These conditions need be maintained only long enough to dry off the surface layers, the period varying roughly from half a day to four days depending on the species and thickness being dried. The appropriate schedule conditions should then be established by gradual stages.

1.7 Mixed Loads
As mentioned in section 9.1.1, it is inadvisable to mix different species and thicknesses in the same kiln, but when such mixing is quite unavoidable, the drying must be carried out in accordance with a schedule which is suitable for the species or thickness which requires the mildest treatment.

2 Modifications during a run
When drying a load of any type for the first time the kiln operator should select from the twelve standard schedules the one which appears to be suitable for the species concerned, decide whether any modification to it is necessary in the light of what has been said in the foregoing paragraphs and then commence the treatment accordingly. It should be clearly understood, however, that the operator should not always adhere strictly to a predetermined schedule regardless of the way the load behaves.

The operator should keep the load under observation so far as possible, and if unacceptable amounts of checking or splitting begin to appear he should raise the humidity or at least delay the scheduled changes in the air conditions. Similarly, if he observes that the timber is distorting unduly or that there are signs of collapse developing, he should refrain from making the increases in temperature scheduled for the later stages of the run.

Reference is made in Appendix E to the influence of kiln conditions on the development of various forms of degrade and to the steps which can be taken to avoid or minimise such defects.

3 Modifications based on experience
The listing of only twelve standard schedules is a compromise and it will be obvious that no one schedule can be equally well suited for all the species in the group for which it is suggested. It may be observed, for instance, that in none of the schedules is the commencing humidity lower than 70 per cent. There are, however, a few species eg abura, obeche and utile, which can be dried very rapidly from the surface without checking and the drying of such tolerant species can undoubtedly be commenced safely at humidities below 70 per cent.

There are, moreover, several other factors which may make it advantageous to deviate from the standard schedule. The use to which the timber is to be put is obviously important, since this determines the amount of degrade that can be accepted in the dried material. For some purposes a certain amount of checking and splitting is no great detriment, and for such purposes timber can be dried at lower humidities and hence faster than when it is necessary to prevent checks from developing. The various forms of distortion are clearly much less important if the dried timber is to be resawn into small pieces than if it is to be used as long, wide boards. There is a tendency, particularly when hardwoods are dried from the green, for greater distortion to occur as the drying temperature is increased. If there is no necessity to keep distortion to a minimum, higher temperatures than those suggested in the standard schedules can be employed to promote faster drying.

The initial quality of the timber also has some bearing on the most satisfactory schedule that can be applied. Straight grained timber free from knots, shakes and other defects is not so liable to distort as timber of poorer quality and in general is likely to tolerate more severe drying conditions, though clear, knot-free boards of some species may suffer damage in the form of long, straight checks if dried too quickly. Quarter-sawn timber is less prone to checking and usually less likely to distort than plain-sawn timber of the same species, and if dried separately will withstand more severe treatment. Again, squares or narrow boards are less susceptible to checking and splitting than wider pieces of the same species and thickness, and can be dried more quickly at appreciably lower humidities, providing that, if they are in short lengths, the ends are protected with a moisture resistant coating to prevent the development of end checking.

Kiln operators who have to dry the same type of load repeatedly are therefore strongly urged to use their experience and judgement in order to arrive at the schedule best suited to their particular material. Nearly always the aim should be to bring the loads to a condition satisfactory for their intended use in the shortest possible time. If the operators find that, after conducting the first few runs in accordance with the schedule originally selected, the degrade is well within acceptable limits, they should shorten the drying time in the next run by raising the temperature by 5°C and/or lowering the humidity by 5 per cent at each stage. If satisfactory results are still obtained with this slightly more severe schedule, further modifications of the same order should gradually be made until an optimum treatment has been evolved.

After long experience with the same type of load, it is sometimes possible to apply a schedule on a time basis, the changes in temperature and humidity being made and the run terminated at prescribed times after the commencement of drying. This has the obvious advantage that the operator can dispense with the periodic weighing of samples, but owing to the very variable nature of timber it is always advisable to test representative samples for final moisture content before unstacking is commenced.

9.5 Conditioning treatment

Whatever the drying schedule applied to a load of timber, a stage is very often reached near the end of the kiln run when many of the samples, after re-estimation (9.2.3), indicate that the desired final moisture content has been attained or passed whilst others show that they need further drying. Such a variation is a result of inequalities in initial moisture content or of inherent differences in drying properties from piece to piece in the load. It sometimes stems also from non-uniformity of drying conditions in the kiln stack.

When the specification or the end use for the dried timber demands a limited deviation from the final average moisture content or an absolute maximum for any one piece, it is necessary to abandon the schedule and apply what is termed a 'conditioning treatment' (known in the USA and some other countries as an 'equalising treatment').

It is usually expedient to continue the drying until the driest sample is at a moisture content 2 or 3 per cent below the final average required and then to raise the relative humidity to a level which, combined with the prevailing temperature, will bring the EMC up to the value required.

As an example, suppose that a load of beech is to be dried to a specified average of 12 per cent and that the moisture contents of the samples range from 9 per cent in a plain-sawn sample on the air inlet side to 16 per cent in a quarter-sawn piece in the slowest drying part of the stack. The scheduled temperature at this stage would be 65°C and the relative humidity 30 per cent and these conditions, as seen from Figure 1 correspond with an EMC of 5 per cent. By increasing the relative humidity to 73 per cent, the EMC becomes 12 per cent and these conditions will tend to wet the drier boards but at the same time allow the wetter ones to continue drying so that all pieces will gradually converge towards the 12 per cent moisture content specified.

The drying of the wetter boards, however, will be much slower than hitherto for the immediate effect of the higher humidity will be to add moisture to the dried surface layers of the material and the moisture gradient promoting flow from the wetter core to the surface will be decreased.

Conditioning is thus inevitably rather a slow process and when, in the drying of a thick refractory species it is important to ensure that no pieces are above a specified maximum moisture content, an alternative procedure may be adopted. When the driest samples in the case already cited reach about 9 per cent moisture content, and further drying towards the 5 per cent EMC would result in excessive distortion, the relative humidity should be raised to 58 per cent giving kiln air EMC conditions of 9 per cent. This will ensure that the driest material ceases to dry and at the same time the wettest will dry faster than if the final EMC of 12 per cent had been applied straight away.

For the reasons already given, a high degree of uniformity must not be expected and a final spread of ±2 per cent moisture content may in general be taken as being the best obtainable for most practical purposes. In the drying of thick, dense hardwoods these limits cannot be achieved without excessively long conditioning periods. The higher the required average moisture content the more difficult it becomes to obtain uniformity.

Apart from bringing the moisture content of all the pieces in a kiln closer to the desired value, the application of a conditioning treatment is also beneficial because it tends in a similar manner to promote a more uniform distribution of moisture throughout the cross-section of each piece in the load. This can be of particular importance when the timber is to be re-sawn or deeply machined thus exposing the wood in the inner zone.

For the convenience of operators, the relationships between the average equilibrium moisture content of wood and the wet- and dry-bulb temperatures of the air is given in Table FI.

9.6 Casehardening relief treatment

It is often desirable and sometimes absolutely essential to relieve and balance the casehardening stresses which normally develop during drying (see 3.4).

The method of doing this consists of applying a high humidity treatment which moistens the outer layers of the timber so that they try to expand upon the core. Strains are thereby induced which are opposite to, and so tend to neutralize, those previously induced by the normal shrinkage during drying. Just as the casehardening was caused by the inability of the surface layers to shrink freely, so it is relieved by their inability to expand fully when moistened by the high humidity treatment.

The actual treatment is usually carried out just before the end of the kiln run by raising the humidity for periods of 2 to 8 hours according to the severity of the stresses as indicated by the prong tests (see 3.4). The relief is quicker and more effective if carried out at high temperatures as these render the wood more plastic. A suitable treatment is one in which the relative humidity is raised to 90 per cent whilst at the same time the temperature is raised 10 to 15°C above that at which the kiln was running. Should the kiln be already running at a high temperature (80°C or over), it will not generally be found necessary to raise the temperature further, nor is it always easy in practice to achieve the conditions quickly as the live steam demand is considerable.

When the stresses have been relieved satisfactorily, test prongs may turn outward slightly, but after exposure in a room they will finally become almost parallel.

The conditioning treatment referred to in 9.5 is in itself a form of relief treatment which will occasionally be found sufficient for the purpose of reducing or balancing casehardening stresses.

In the event of a relief treatment being unduly prolonged at near saturation conditions, the timber surface layers may be overstrained, producing the condition known as reversed casehardening. Test prongs cut from timber in which strong reverse strains have been induced will turn outwards and will remain as in Figure 5b even after drying in a room.

Only experience will tell the operator just what relief treatment is likely to give the best results with any particular kiln load. (See also 7.4.)

9.7 Care of dried timber

It need hardly be said that dried timber after its removal from the kiln should be fully protected from the weather. For instance, any loads of kiln dried timber transported by lorry should be well sheeted down in wet weather.

In factories where kiln dried timber is taken directly from the kilns into the re-saw mill, care should be taken to ensure that the material is cooled throughout before it is sawn. Fine checks are very liable to occur on warm, fresh-cut ends of hardwoods, and in ripping or deeping, slight distortion may also result from the exposure of interior zones which are warmer than the surface layers.

In well-planned factories having dry storage space into which bogie loads of kiln dried timber can be run, it is advantageous to leave the wood in stick for 2 to 3 days during which time any moisture differences and gradients existing after the kiln treatment will tend to diminish.

Ideally, of course, dried timber should be kept in atmospheric conditions corresponding roughly to the moisture content at which the wood is required when manufactured. In a heated store the equilibrium moisture content can be adjusted to some extent by varying the amount of heating, for this in turn will control the humidity, and the efficient operator can, with the aid of hygrometer tables and an equilibrium moisture content chart, obtain approximately the conditions required.

Dehumidifiers controlled by humidistats provide an alternative method of keeping timber stores at the required EMC conditions using little or no heat.

When kiln dried timber has to be kept for any length of time in an unheated shed or store, it should be unstacked as soon as it is quite cool and tightly close-piled so that only the outer boards or planks will change much in moisture content. Short dimension stock with a high proportion of end grain exposed is liable to pick up moisture rather rapidly, and if piles of such material have to be left for long in open sheds in the winter months they should, if possible, be covered with tarpaulins or plastic sheets.

Chapter 10 Miscellaneous kiln treatments

In addition to the normal kiln treatments comprising the drying schedule, conditioning and casehardening relief treatments, there are occasions when special treatments have to be applied. These include 'reconditioning', 'steaming', and treatments to kill fungal growth and to sterilise insect-infested timber.

10.1 Reconditioning

Reference has already been made under section 3.5 to a form of degrade known as collapse which commonly occurs in the drying of certain species of *Eucalyptus* and is by no means unusual in other species. For example, home-grown oak and elm may collapse to quite a serious extent if dried to too severe a schedule.

It is usually possible to observe under a microscope the distorted and collapsed appearance of the cells in badly collapsed timber, and the 'wash-boarding' effect produced on the surfaces of boards is often very obvious. Certain woods, such as oak and ash, can be affected by a form of collapse which leads to abnormal shrinkage but not to the observable caving in of cells or to the surface undulations normally associated with this form of degrade. In both cases, however, with some few exceptions, it is possible to remove much of the excess shrinkage, and of the accompanying distortions of the cross-section, by the application of what is termed a reconditioning treatment.

This treatment, which was first used commercially in Australia, consists essentially of heating the timber to a temperature of 100°C (212°F) at a relative humidity of 100 per cent, ie 'steaming'. The treatment, if applied for periods of from 4 to 8 hours, depending upon thickness, degree of collapse etc, will usually cause most of the collapsed or abnormally shrunken cells to resume their more normal shape, with a consequent marked improvement in the general appearance and quality of the material. As an indication of the improvement that may be effected by such means, the cross-section of a board of 'Tasmanian oak' before and after reconditioning is illustrated in Plate 8.

Why the steamed, collapsed wood behaves in this manner is not fully understood, but it is probable that the wood is rendered sufficiently plastic to permit the latent and residual stresses opposing collapse within the material to become effective, bringing the distorted and compressed cells back to their normal shape. Tests have indicated that the best results are achieved when the timber is at an average moisture content of about 15 per cent, and that the moisture pick-up of a load of reasonable dimensions will amount to little more than one or two per cent. Even so, some further drying will often be necessary and, with this in mind, it would obviously be advantageous to carry out the steaming treatment in the drying kiln. Unfortunately, however, this high temperature/high humidity treatment tends to prove very detrimental to the fittings and general internal equipment of a kiln and, in Australia, it is commonly carried out in a specially built concrete reconditioning chamber separate from the drying kiln proper. Such a chamber consists simply of a well-insulated room, or box, fitted with a large-size steam spray, by means of which the necessary conditions can be quickly obtained.

Unless collapse is of common occurrence and of a serious nature it is open to doubt whether a separate reconditioning treatment would be justified, bearing in mind the cost of the steaming chamber, the double handling and the quantities of steam involved. A further point to be considered is that the high temperatures tend to darken certain timbers; moreover, the wetting and subsequent re-drying of the surfaces which occur in a reconditioning treatment may open up surfaces checks that had formed in the early stages of kiln drying but had closed up and become invisible at the conclusion of the run.

It may be added that wood which is badly distorted but not obviously collapsed, may sometimes be considerably improved by a reconditioning treatment.

10.2 Steaming

Although the term 'steaming' is sometimes used in connection with high humidity treatments for casehardening relief, sterilisation etc, it should strictly be applied only to treatments in steam at the boiling point, ie 100°C (212°F) or over, as in reconditioning. It is common practice on the Continent to subject green beech to a steaming treatment of three to four days' duration before it is seasoned. Such a treatment thoroughly sterilises the timber but does not dry it to any very appreciable extent. The change in colour is probably the only other important advantage to be derived from the treatment. Most woods tend to darken if subjected to high temperatures, especially when in the green condition, and beech tends to assume a dark pink or reddish colour as a result of steaming. A more uniform tone is obtained throughout the material, and this is considered to be desirable by the manufacturers of certain specialised articles. It would, of course, be possible to steam wood in this manner in a normal type of drying kiln, given adequate steam spray pipes and pressure, but as mentioned earlier it is not to be recommended as general practice because of the adverse effect on the kiln. Separate steaming chambers may be provided but the process may then call for double handling and it also makes considerable demands on the steam supply. These disadvantages, as a rule, more than offset the few advantages that might result from the application of this treatment to the timber before seasoning.

It should be mentioned, perhaps, that some colouring effects and also, in certain species, some partial recovery from collapse, can be obtained by subjecting the wood to saturated air at temperatures 10 or 20°C below the boiling point.

10.3 Killing fungal growths

Certain fungal growths, including those likely to discolour the timber, tend to persist or even to flourish at the moderate temperature and high humidity conditions that often prevail in a kiln during the early stages of drying green material (see 3.6.1). Surface mould growths may even be sufficient to impede the flow of air between the layers of timber in a kiln load.

When such a growth occurs it becomes advisable to subject it to a lethal treatment, even though it is realised that the drying of the timber must eventually prove effective in arresting all further development. It can also be an advantage, at the start of a kiln run, to sterilise any species which is particularly susceptible to stain, so that any fungus spores present are killed before they have time to develop.

A treatment found to be generally effective in such cases consists of raising the temperature to 70°C (158°F) and the humidity to 100 per cent and maintaining these conditions for three hours. The timber, after treatment, is not immune from further attack and it may be deemed necessary to apply a similar treatment again at a later stage in the run. After the treatment the kiln conditions should be returned to normal, but it is important that the cooling should be carried out slowly and at high humidities to avoid excessive surface drying. It is suggested that the wet-bulb depression during this period should never be greater than about 3 or 4°C and even less when dealing with a load of green timber.

10.4 Sterilisation of insect-infested timber

Timber drying kilns are sometimes found useful for sterilising timber which has been attacked by *Lyctus* powder-post beetles or other wood-boring insects. *Lyctus* beetles cause serious damage to the sapwood of certain hardwoods, notably oak and ash, and are undoubtedly more important from the commercial aspect than other pests. They do not attack green timber but the infestation may begin while the timber is being air dried or while it is held in store in a seasoned condition.

Timber to be sterilised should be stacked in the kiln in much the same way as for drying and the same care should be taken to see that the circulating air moves uniformly through the stack. It is, however, permissible since the planks or boards are usually already fairly dry, to space the piling sticks appreciably further apart than they would need to be if the same material were to be dried from a green condition. Dimension stock can often be 'self-crossed' with resulting economy of space and without the risk of staining that would arise if it were green when stacked. It must be remembered, however, that 'self-crossing' has the effect of increasing the thickness of timber through which heat has to penetrate and the time of treatment should be adjusted accordingly. When veneers have to be sterilised they can be made up into packs of a convenient thickness and these packs arranged in layers separated by sticks. The length of treatment should be the same as for solid timber of thickness equal to that of the packs.

Experiments have shown that *Lyctus* beetles in all stages of development can be killed by subjecting them to air at temperatures of 45°C (113°F) or higher, and relative humidities of 60 per cent and upwards. The period

Recommended treatments for kiln sterilisation of *Lycus*-infested timber

Kiln conditions			Period of exposure for timber of different thickness (hours)					Approximate corresponding equilibrium moisture content per cent
Temp °C	°F	Relative humidity per cent	25 mm (1 in or less)	38 mm ($1\frac{1}{2}$ in)	50 mm (2in)	62 mm ($2\frac{1}{2}$ in)	75 mm (3 in)	
60	140	100	3	4	5	6	7	25–30
60	140	80	3	4	5	6	7	15
57	135	100	4	5	6	7	8	25–30
57	135	80	4	5	6	7	8	15
57	135	60	6	7	8	9	10	10
55	130	100	8	9	10	11	12	25–30
55	130	80	8	9	10	11	12	15
55	130	60	10	11	12	13	14	10
52	125	100	38	39	40	41	42	25–30
52	125	80	38	39	40	41	42	15
52	125	60	46	47	48	49	50	10

of exposure necessary decreases as the temperature and humidity are increased and at 55°C (130°F) and 100 per cent rh, for instance, it is as short as 1½ hours. When a kiln load of material has to be sterilised it is, of course, essential that every portion of it should be exposed to lethal conditions. Since in many kilns there is liable to be some variation of temperature throughout the load, it is advisable that the conditions indicated by the control hygrometer should be more severe than are strictly necessary to kill the beetles, and also that the control hygrometer should be placed on the outlet side of the stack. The table of recommended treatments given below has been prepared on the assumption that the temperatures in some parts of a kiln may be as much as 5°C (9°F) lower than that shown by the control hygrometer. The periods of exposure in this table include an allowance for the time required for the timber to become heated throughout its thickness, and an additional factor of safety.

The duration of the treatment is determined principally by the thickness of the timber. When selecting a treatment, however, the kiln operator should consider the effect it will have on the moisture content and general condition of the load, and the temperature and humidity should be chosen so that the equilibrium moisture content is not widely different from the average moisture content of the timber. Treatment at 100 per cent humidity is liable to wet the surfaces of the timber and should not be applied if there are checks or splits in the timber which have closed up before the treatment. In any event, its application should be confined to loads with an average moisture content of 25 per cent or higher. On the other hand, timber which has only been air dried prior to sterilisation would dry rapidly from the surfaces if it were exposed to a humidity as low as 60 per cent and new checking might develop. Treatment at this humidity should therefore be limited to loads with a moisture content of 12 per cent or less. To avoid wetting the timber by condensation during the warming up of a load, it is advisable to maintain a wet-bulb depression of about 7°C (12°F) throughout the warming process.

It will be observed that the conditions necessary for the sterilisation of *Lyctus*-infested timber are incorporated in most of the kiln schedules recommended by this Laboratory. This is certainly true of Schedules B, C and E to M inclusive, and it is very probable that the conditions laid down in Schedule D would also prove lethal to the insects. With any of these schedules, the application of a conditioning treatment at comparatively high humidity at the conclusion of the drying run would definitely ensure that the load had been sterilised. When timber is dried in accordance with Schedule A, the temperature and humidity necessary for sterilisation are not reached, and when sterilisation of the load is required, a suitable treatment should be given at the end of the run. It is perhaps worth mentioning that departures from the recommended schedules have often to be made for quite good reasons, and it follows therefore that timber is not necessarily sterilised merely because it has been kiln dried. It must also be emphasised that heat sterilisation does not render timber immune from re-infestation. There is, however, no evidence to support the suggestion that kiln sterilisation actually leaves the timber in a condition more susceptible to attack.

Kiln treatment can also be used for the destruction of insects in manufactured articles whether constructed of solid of laminated timber, but considerable care is necessary to prevent damage to surface finishes and the weakening of glued joints. When such articles are treated, particular attention should be paid to the avoidance of condensation during the warming up of the kiln and it is probably advisable not to exceed a temperature of 55°C (130°F) nor a relative humidity of 60 per cent.

Full data are not available on the efficacy against other wood-boring insects of the treatments given in the table on page 85. Of these, powder-post beetles of the family, Bostrychidae, most of which are found in tropical timbers and are usually larger than *Lyctus*, are most often concerned. Results of the few tests carried out indicate that the smaller members of this family are destroyed at conditions lethal to *Lyctus* but there is some doubt as to whether this holds good for the larger species. Laboratory tests have shown that the conditions of temperature and humidity lethal to *Lyctus* are more than adequate to destroy grubs of the common funiture beetle (*Anobium punctatum*).

Little information is available on sterilisation treatments lethal to longhorn beetles (Cerambycidae) and wood-wasps (Siricidae). However, treatments approved in Australia under the quarantine regulations include:

a Heat applied at a temperature of (74°C) 165°F and maintained for a period which is determined by the maximum thickness of the timber as shown in the following table.

Thickness of timber	**Length of treatment**
Less than 2 in	6 hours
Less than 3 in more than 2 in	8 hours
Less than 4 in more than 3 in	10 hours
Less than 6 in more than 4 in	14 hours
Less than 12 in more than 6 in	26 hours

The temperature in the centre of the stack must reach (74°C) 165°F before the period of treatment commences.

b Kiln drying to 14 per cent moisture content or lower. The timber must be dried to the standard kiln drying procedure and the amount of heat applied must be equal to that outlined in (a) above.

Chapter 11 Some other methods of drying

11.0 Introduction

The methods of drying timber using air as the drying medium have been described in earlier sections, the commonly used ones, namely air drying and kiln drying, naturally receiving the fullest attention.

There are several other quite different methods and, although none of them are in general commercial use, all those concerned with timber drying should have some knowledge of the principles and practice involved and of the various limitations which make unlikely their adoption on a wide scale.

Certain criteria must be applied when assessing the potential value of any new method of timber drying. Primarily, it must produce in a reasonably short time timber dried to the level and uniformity of moisture content required for any particular purpose, without causing such degrade that the wood is unfit for that purpose. For general commercial drying, any method must be capable of handling quite a wide variety of species and sizes and the overall cost of drying must compare favourably with that of orthodox methods.

A novel process which speeds up timber drying does not always prove advantageous when everything is taken into account, but considerable benefits can accrue if drying can be achieved in a matter of hours instead of days. For instance, when items can be dried very rapidly by radio frequency heating (see 11.3), drying on a conveyor system becomes a possibility, considerably reducing handling costs and the stocks which have to be held, and the whole pattern of production may be changed.

Other factors may favour some of the special methods of drying. In the solvent seasoning of softwoods, for instance, if there is a good market for some of the chemical by-products the process can become economically viable. Timber dried at very high temperatures is rendered more stable than that dried at normal temperatures. Drying processes carried out in cylinders can be followed immediately by preservative treatments when required.

11.1 Chemical methods

Two methods involving the use of chemicals come under this heading although the roles which the chemicals play differ widely. In solvent seasoning a chemical is used to extract water from wood by entrainment, whereas in so called 'chemical seasoning' a salt is used only to control the rate of moisture vapour movement through and from the wood being dried in air, either out-of-doors or in drying chambers.

1 Solvent seasoning

Solvent seasoning consists essentially of subjecting timber to the action of a liquid which has a high affinity for water and which is miscible with it. By passing such a liquid over wet timber the water is removed by entrainment and not by evaporation, so that solvent seasoning is almost unique in that heat is not essential to the process of drying. The solvent can permeate into and readily remove water from the sapwood portions of a plank but it cannot be so effective in the heartwood of impermeable species. In practice, the solvent is heated to around 40 to 50° C and the drying rate is further increased by the rapid heat transfer from liquid to wood.

In a plant operated for some years by the Western Pine Association in Oregon the resinous pine was stacked on end in a tightly sealed drying chamber and sprayed continuously with hot acetone. The mixture of acetone, water and extractives was re-circulated but a proportion of it drawn off so that it could be distilled to recover pure acetone and separate the water and the extractives. In the second stage of the process, heated air was blown over the wood to complete the drying and remove the acetone.

The drying of ponderosa pine in this plant was from three to four times faster than that in orthodox kilns but the basic cost of drying per unit volume was nevertheless much higher. Solvent seasoning was shown to be an economic proposition only when the timber was upgraded by removal of the resin and when the extractives obtained as a by-product could readily be sold. No major commercial use of the method has been reported and the conditions under which it could be applied successfully do not exist in the UK.

2 Salt seasoning

Salt seasoning is the term generally applied to the drying of timber with the aid of chemicals which are used not to effect the actual drying but to control the rate of surface evaporation and hence moisture distribution and stresses set up during either air drying or kiln drying.

Green wood is treated with a hygroscopic chemical such as common salt or urea. This is done either by immersion in a strong solution of the salt in water or by spreading the dry salt on top of each layer whilst bulk-piling the timber as it comes from the saw. Either method takes a number of days for the salts to penetrate sufficiently to become effective, depending on the transverse permeability of the species being treated.

When the timber so treated is dried, the hygroscopic salt lowers the vapour pressure and so keeps the moisture content of the outer layers higher than normal, but moisture passes from the untreated inner zones into the treated outer layers and thence into the air. Tensile stresses are much lower and so surface checking is greatly reduced or entirely eliminated. In air drying, the times taken to dry are inevitably somewhat increased by the treatment but in kiln drying faster drying can safely be achieved by using humidities below those in the normal schedules for untreated material.

It has been found that pre-treatment with a salt makes it possible to dry, without surface checking, difficult items such as large section Douglas fir, and bowls or cylinders of hardwood can be dried without the familiar V-checks to the centre developing. *Plate 32.*

Common salt is one of the most effective chemicals to use but solutions have to incorporate corrosion inhibitors to prevent the corrosion of metals coming into contact with the treated wood. Urea does not corrode metals other than copper but tends to discolour the wood treated and in practice this discoloration increases the longer the solution in a soaking tank is used.

It is very difficult to get an effective amount of chemical into impervious woods such as oak. Prolonged immersion of these species in a warm, saturated solution can actually cause the core of planks to dry out faster than the surface layers and the stresses set up can be sufficient to cause honeycombing to take place.

One of the disadvantages of salt-treated timber is that it absorbs more moisture than untreated wood and tends to 'sweat' when the relative humidity of the air around it is above about 80 per cent.

Salt treatment adds to the overall cost of drying and is likely to be economic only for items which cannot otherwise be dried satisfactorily. Modern glues and laminating techniques have to a great extent removed the need for drying large sections of timber.

More recent than salt seasoning is the use of high molecular weight polyethylene glycol (PEG), a water soluble wax-like substance, for controlling checking mainly by its anti-shrink effect. By immersion of green wood in a warm solution of PEG in water for a period of a week or so, enough wax gets into the wood substance of the outer layers to reduce shrinkage there by its bulking effect.

PEG has been used with some success in the conservation of waterlogged antiquities but its application as an aid to drying has been limited to items such as green carvings, decorative discs, cross-sectional discs, rifle furniture etc, which can stand the extra cost of the PEG treatment. Many of the species which are prone to surface check are relatively impermeable across the grain and, as with salt or urea, it is difficult to introduce enough PEG to be fully effective.

11.2 Boiling methods

In normal drying the moisture moves to the surface as a result of vapour pressure differences set up by moisture gradients in the wood, and leaves the surfaces when the vapour pressure of the ambient air is lower than that of the wood surfaces.

When the wood temperature is raised above the boiling point of the water it holds, air is expelled and an absolute pressure difference is set up so that as heat is supplied so will the water be boiled off irrespective of the relative humidity of the surrounding atmosphere. Provided that sufficient heat can be supplied and the wood permits the steam generated to escape, very rapid drying can be achieved.

The term 'boiling method' is used to cover the processes described below in which various means are employed to supply the heat required to boil off the water from the wood.

1 Boiling in oily liquids

One way of drying wood rapidly, by boiling off the water as fast as its permeability permits, is to immerse it in a hot oily liquid which has a boiling point of well over 100°C. The heat transfer from the hot liquid to the wood is rapid and the wood is quickly brought up to the temperature at which water is boiled off. This temperature depends on the permeability of the wood, being 100°C for permeable species whilst free water is present and then rising as the moisture content falls.

Since the surface layers are heated and dried in advance of the interior and the relative humidity within the hot liquid is very low, a steep moisture gradient quickly develops and considerable surface checking occurs in some species. Severe casehardening is inevitable and there is no means of relieving the stresses.

The method is not generally a practical one as it leaves the wood in an oily state unfit for most purposes but it is used to a certain extent to dry timber down to fibre saturation point prior to impregnation with preservatives.

An example is the process known as 'Boultonizing', in which items such as sleepers, poles and posts are loaded into a treatment cylinder and immersed in a heated oily preservative such as creosote. When a vacuum is applied the free water in the sapwood boils off at a temperature well below 100°C and this preliminary drying is followed by the appropriate impregnation treatment. Thus the costs of prior air drying and double handling are eliminated.

The Boulton process has been used on Douglas fir and hemlock on the west coast of USA and Canada but is seldom applied in the UK.

2 Vacuum drying
The vacuum drying of many substances, such as chemicals and foodstuffs, makes use of the fact that the boiling point of water is substantially lowered when the pressure of the atmosphere over it is lowered. For example, if the normal pressure of 101 kN/m² (14·7 psi) is lowered to 20 kN/m² (2·9 psi) the boiling point is lowered from 100°C to 60°C.

In processes developed to apply vacuum drying to wood, the load is run into cylinders similar to those used for impregnation treatments and is heated up to 100°C by steaming or by immersion in boiling water. When the steam is shut off or the boiling water is drawn off and a vacuum is immediately applied, some of the moisture in the wood boils off rapidly. Latent heat of evaporation is essential, however, and drying ceases as soon as the specific heat made available by the fall in temperature of the wood and the moisture in it is used up; the vacuum by itself causes no drying.

There is no easy way of conveying heat to a load of timber in a cylinder under vacuum. In the absence of air, there is virtually no convection, heating by conduction is impracticable and radiant heat around the perimeter can only warm up the outside of the stack.

Recourse is therefore made to reheating the wood by steaming and further drying is achieved by drawing a second vacuum. The drying in the second cycle is less, as there is less specific heat in the drier wood and so with repeated cycles the drying rate falls off. Furthermore, as the wood gets drier it tends to re-absorb moisture during the steaming period and it is therefore difficult to attain low final moisture contents by vacuum drying. Hot air could be used instead of steam for re-warming but this method would be slower and would involve some risk of damaging the timber.

In spite of these limitations attempts have been made from time to time to promote the use of vacuum drying plants in the timber trade. These have followed reasonable results obtained by inventors during small scale tests in which radiant heat could reach the two or three specimens in a pilot plant. The vacuum drying plants were expensive to install in relation to the amount of timber held and, in drying to 20 to 25 per cent by repeated cycles, the times taken were not short enough to compensate for the small capacity.

3 Drying in superheated steam
Timber can be dried in an ordinary forced draught kiln using superheated steam instead of air to heat the wood and carry away the moisture evaporated, provided that both the heating and steam spray are adequate and the kiln shell is very well insulated.

Steam is introduced until the wet-bulb temperature reaches 100°C, all air is expelled and the heating pipes are then controlled to superheat the circulating steam to the desired level, which may finally be up to 120°C or more. Vents must be hinged to open freely to ensure that the pressure in the kiln cannot build up above that of the atmosphere.

The wood is heated by the superheated steam to 100°C, free water is boiled off and the need for steam from the spray ceases. Drying takes place from the surfaces, but moisture movement from the interior is rapid at such high temperatures. As the wood dries below fibre saturation point its temperature rises and when it reaches the dry-bulb temperature drying ceases. Wood in superheated steam thus comes into equilibrium at a moisture content related to the degree of superheat and this fact facilitates the control of the drying and application of a conditioning period as in ordinary drying. At 105°C dry-bulb and 100°C wet-bulb, for instance, data obtained by German research workers show that the EMC is approximately 10 per cent.

The fan system in a superheated steam kiln must be capable of circulating rapidly very large volumes of the steam otherwise the lag in drying rate across the stack becomes excessive due to the steam cooling very quickly as it gives up its heat to the timber.

Since no air interchange is involved in ridding the kiln chamber of surplus steam coming from the wood, the thermal efficiency of the process can be greater than that of orthodox kilning provided that the kiln shell is well insulated.

Timber can be dried very rapidly in superheated steam and the resulting material is less hygroscopic and more stable in use than that dried at lower temperatures.

The shrinkage accompanying drying from the green is greater, however, and in many species collapse is liable to occur. Resin exudation, loosening of knots and darkening in colour all increase, due to the combination of steam and high temperature.

Superheated steam drying, with its scalding kiln conditions, is not easy for the operator. In the rapid drying conditions, overdrying and hence extra distortion is liable to occur and the gradients and spread in final moisture content are large before conditioning is applied.

Deterioration of masonry kiln shells and any ferrous equipment is rapid and this was one of the reasons why the superheated steam drying of softwoods on the west coast of USA and Canada was discontinued. Present day all-aluminium kilns withstand the conditions better and the method has been used to a certain extent in Germany and Scandinavia.

Temperatures above 100°C are now used mainly in conjunction with wet-bulb temperatures of less than 100°C. This is often referred to as 'high temperature drying' and in principle is no different from orthodox kiln drying in that the drying medium is a mixture of air and superheated vapour. In fact it is merely kiln drying to schedules using temperatures higher than those in the most severe PRL Schedule, M, and they are applied only to softwoods since nearly all hardwoods suffer from extra degrade of one kind or another at these high temperatures.

4 Vapour drying

Vapour drying is a patented process in which timber is subjected in a closed system to the vapour of an organic chemical such as xylene or perchloroethylene with a boiling point well over that of water. The hot vapour condensing on the cooler wood promotes very rapid heating and boiling off of the free water. The rate of drying is increased by the faster movement of moisture through the timber at the high temperatures reached and the steep moisture gradient set up because the surface layers boil first.

The plant for this process is shown diagrammatically in Figure 26. The drying agent is boiled in the steam-heated evaporator and the vapours pass into the drying cylinder. A mixture of the surplus vapour and the steam from the wood passes into a condenser and the two immiscible liquids into a separator. Water, being heavier than the organic chemical, can be drawn off and measurement by flow meter gives a good estimation of the drying achieved. When drying is completed the evaporator is shut off and a vacuum is drawn. This causes most of the drying agent which has entered the hot wood to re-evaporate.

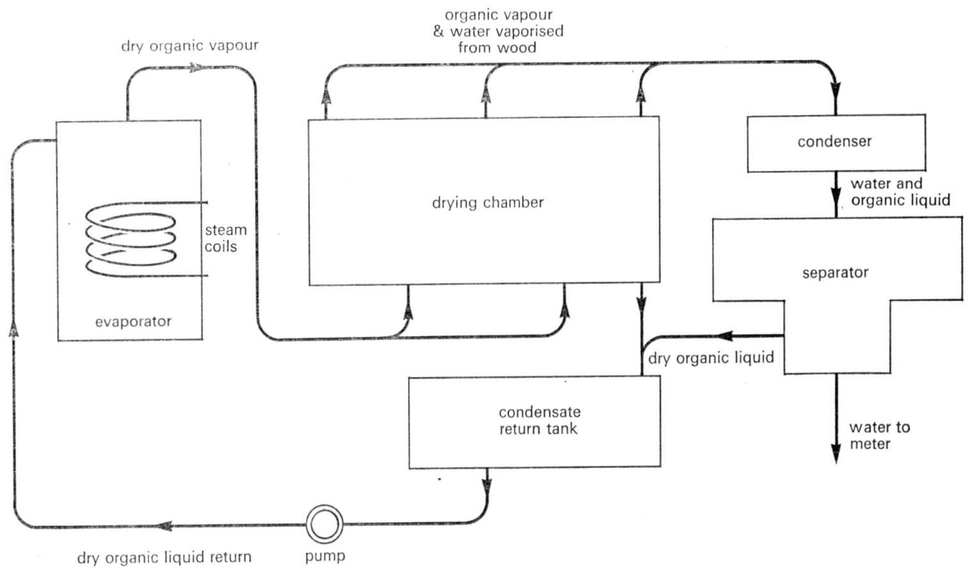

Figure 26 *Flow diagram of vapour drying process*

The vapour drying process was developed by the Taylor Colquitt Co of America for drying poles and railway sleepers which were dried to 35 to 40 per cent moisture content in a matter of only 10 to 16 hours. The drying was followed immediately by a full pressure/vacuum preservative treatment carried out in the same plant, thus reducing handling to a minimum.

In vapour drying, a mass of fine checks tend to develop instead of the long deep ones common in the air drying of sleepers and poles. Whilst acceptable for such items they would render timber unfit for many other uses and attempts in America and Australia to modify the process for general drying were only partially successful. Permeable species were dried in as little as 5 to 10 per cent of the time usually taken in ordinary drying, but impermeable species required the application of a vacuum to lower the temperature of drying and took about 30 per cent of the normal kiln drying time. The moisture variation, both across the section and between individual pieces in a load, and casehardening, all tended to be excessive and for many end-uses a conditioning treatment would have to be applied to the vapour dried timber.

Vapour drying involves a comparatively costly and complex plant and more highly skilled operators than orthodox drying. It is very doubtful whether the rapid drying achieved could offset the disadvantages outlined, except in the case of the drying and preservative treatment of a limited range of items. For some of these the 'Boultonizing' process referred to in 11.2.1 may be a better proposition.

5 Press drying

In press drying the timber is heated to the boiling point of the water content and dried very rapidly by keeping it under pressure between the hot plates of a press. The method is unique in that the heat essential for evaporation is conveyed to the wood by conduction.

The standard treatment in the process patented and used commercially by A/S Junckers Savvaerk of Denmark for drying beech flooring strips, consists of keeping the platens of the press at around 165°C and applying a pressure of 1172 kN/m² (170 psi) on the single layers of wood between them.

Drying 30 mm beech from green to 2 to 3 per cent moisture content takes only about 2 hours. This drying is followed by conditioning up to 7 to 8 per cent by placing a load of strips into a cylinder, applying a vacuum and then admitting steam, the treatment taking 4 to 5 hours.

As in most boiling methods, press drying is only successful on boards of permeable species such as beech and birch which allow the steam generated to escape freely. With impermeable species, pressure is generated within the wood and internal rupture ('bursting') often occurs. Even beech must be dried very soon after felling and conversion, for in storage the wood can quickly develop tyloses which block the vessels and render the wood impermeable. A steaming treatment (10.2) following conversion prevents this happening.

Due to the combined effects of high pressure and shrinkage there is a reduction in thickness of up to about 20 per cent when drying beech strips. On the other hand, the width is very little changed and distortion is virtually prevented.

One main advantage of press drying is that it results in a large reduction in the movement in the width of wood with subsequent moisture change. It can halve it in the case of beech, thus making this otherwise unstable species suitable for flooring. This fact, together with the advantages of very rapid drying with little or no distortion or loss in width, accounts for the process being found to be economic in spite of the relatively high cost of the large multi-daylight presses and other equipment involved.

The results of many attempts to apply press drying to species and sizes other than beech strips have not yet been promising enough to encourage any general application of the method.

11.3 Drying by radio frequency heating

The application of radio frequency power to dielectric materials containing moisture, such as wood, affords a method of heating and drying which differs markedly from all others. In a piece of wood exposed in an alternating field having a frequency of a million or more cycles per second the extremely rapid agitation of the polar molecules causes the wood to heat up simultaneously throughout its mass. In all other methods described the surfaces have to be heated first and the bulk of the material therefore derives its heat only by the comparatively slow process of conduction.

Radio frequency heating is applied in timber drying mainly as a method of promoting very rapid boiling off of the water content. It has also been used to accelerate the drying at temperatures below the boiling point by setting up temperature gradients from centre to surfaces which speed up the transfusion of moisture.

Basically in any RF drying installation the wood is introduced as the dielectric between metal electrodes fed from a generator which converts mains power at 50 cycles per sec into power at radio frequencies. *Fig 27*. To obtain the maximum efficiency the load must be electrically tuned to the generator.

1 Boiling method

Using RF power, extremely rapid heating, boiling and drying of the wood can be achieved provided that its structure allows the steam to escape

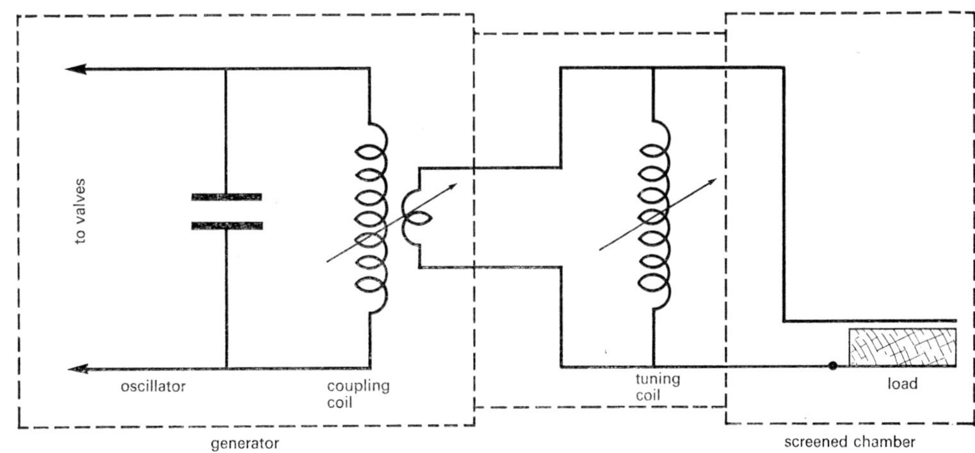

Figure 27 *RF Drying—Circuit diagram showing coupling of load to generator*

freely. The rate of drying then depends on the power concentration obtainable and, in contrast with other methods of drying, is independent of the thickness. For example, 150 mm (6 in) beech squares have been dried satisfactorily from green to 12 per cent in about an hour with the interior finally slightly drier than the outer layers which lose some heat to the surroundings.

The very rapid drying rates obtainable make it feasible to operate a continuous process by passing timber between electrodes on a conveyor as illustrated in Figure 28.

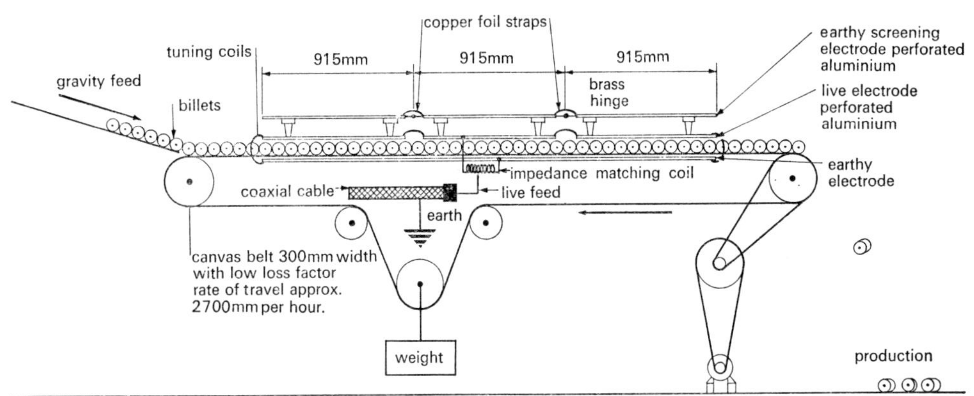

Figure 28 *RF Drying—Continuous dryer for birch billets*

The selective heating which occurs when pieces of differing moisture contents are side by side in an RF field results in the wetter material drying the faster, and when drying is continued to a low moisture content, reasonable uniformity is achieved.

Unfortunately the number of species which are sufficiently permeable to permit the use of the RF boiling method is relatively small; it includes such timbers as beech, birch, boxwood and sycamore. In less permeable species there is always a tendency for pressure to be built up when steam is generated faster than it can escape and internal rupture ('bursting') occurs as in the sample of oak in Plate 33.

The lower the permeability of the wood the more difficult it becomes to control the power input to the low levels essential to avoid bursting, and the technical problems of doing so when heating several pieces at a time are very considerable. It is for such reasons that the 'temperature gradient method' of utilising RF heating has sometimes been employed.

2 Temperature gradient method

By applying a low RF power concentration to timber which is exposed to a flow of cool, moist air over the surfaces, temperature gradients and hence steeper vapour pressure gradients are set up which accelerate the movement of moisture from the interior.

The temperatures employed in this method are nearly always well below boiling point so that the risk of bursting is eliminated, but it is then difficult to prevent the surface layers drying too much in advance of the interior. In species prone to check, therefore, drying times have only been shortened to between one-third and one-fifth of those taken in conventional kilning.

3 Commercial applications of RF drying

RF drying by the boiling method has been applied in the UK to such special items as hardwood squares for shuttles, birch billets for broom-heads, boxwood slats for rules and squares for tool handles.

Several plants have been operated on the Continent, all of the conveyor type and mainly for the drying of beech shoe lasts and furniture squares.

In Russia, drying by the temperature gradient method has been carried out in conventional compartment kilns by introducing a system of RF-fed electrodes at intervals throughout the stacks. In the UK, attempts have been made to develop a drying plant using a combination of air at high temperatures and RF heating applied in regular pulses, and some success has been achieved in the drying of softwoods such as Scots pine, western hemlock and western red cedar.

The main potential advantage of RF drying lies in the very high speed of drying, enabling stocks to be decreased and conveyor systems adopted, giving a steady output of dried material and reducing handling costs, especially of small items.

In spite of persistent efforts to exploit this advantage, the number of commercial applications has remained small. The factors militating against the wider use of RF drying include the limitation of the boiling method to permeable species, the difficulty of imposing restraint to limit the distortion of boards or planks during drying and the costs of the process compared with those of air drying and kiln drying.

The capital cost of an RF drying installation is high, calling for its use night and day, but this involves extra labour costs. There is a loss of around 40 per cent in the conversion of mains to RF power and it takes nearly $1\frac{1}{2}$ kWh of mains power to evaporate every kilogramme of water. RF drying can become more competitive with kiln drying in the case of large section items such as shoe lasts, and in drying from the air dried condition.

The temperature gradient method involves the cost of RF generators and equipment in addition to that of an efficient fan kiln. It may, however, be economically viable in countries with cheap electricity.

Microwave heating may also be applied to the drying of wood and has the advantage that various shaped pieces can be dried more readily in a microwave oven than between RF electrodes. It is still subject, however, to the major drawbacks of RF drying, such as the high cost of plant and power and the difficulty of heating the many low permeability species without damage.

Appendix A Drying properties of timbers

The data on the kiln drying properties of the various species given in this Appendix have been obtained for the most part from tests at the Princes Risborough Laboratory. In many instances the amount of timber available for test was limited and hence only a general indication of the behaviour of the species during drying could be obtained. Information on certain timbers not tested at this Laboratory has been abstracted from reports of laboratories overseas and other reliable sources; such information is denoted by an asterisk.

The standard kiln schedules referred to are set out in Appendix E and guidance on the possibility of modifying these in certain circumstances is given in section 9.4 of this manual.

Average shrinkage values in kiln drying from green to 12 per cent moisture content are given when available so that the decrease in width and thickness likely to occur in the various timbers can be calculated. It must be emphasised that these values are only approximate and some variation about the average must be expected. It should also be pointed out that the shrinkage of any particular timber during drying cannot invariably be taken as a guide to its movement with moisture change when in service.

Drying times

In the method of estimating the probable time taken to dry any particular kiln load of timber, outlined in Appendix C, species are classified into nine groups. For all those species on which there are sufficient data their drying group is indicated in the final column on each page.

† In drying from green to 12% moisture content
* Information derived from sources other than PRL

Commercial name	Botanical species	Kiln schedule suggested	Approx. shrinkage %† Tangential	Radial	Kiln drying characteristics	Drying time group
Abura	*Mitragyna stipulosa*	K	6·5	3·5	Dries very well but distortion and collapse may occur in darker wood regions near the heart	3
Afara	*Terminalia superba*	J			Dries with little or no checking. Distortion very slight	4
Afrormosia	*Pericopsis elata*	J	2·5	1·5	Dries with very little degrade but occasionally fine surface checking troublesome; thick stock tends to retain moist pockets in inner zones	5
Afzelia	*Afzelia* spp	E	1·5	1·0	Dries with little degrade except slight distortion, extension of shakes and fine checking	9
Agba	*Gossweilerodendron balsamiferum*	J	3·0	1·5	Dries with little degrade but gum exudation often heavy	4
Albizia, West African	*Albizia* spp	F			Little degrade but dries very slowly in thick sizes	
Alder	*Alnus glutinosa*	J	6·5	4·0	Dries well and fairly rapidly	
Alstonia	*Alstonia congensis*	H	5·0	3·0	Dries rapidly and well—very little checking—slight distortion	
Antiaris	*Antiaris africana*	A	3·0	1·5	Dries fairly rapidly but with pronounced distortion, especially twist	
Apple	*Malus sylvestris*	A			Dries slowly with tendency to distort	

Ash	*Fraxinus* spp	D	7·0	4·5	Dries with little checking but severe end splits may occur at start. Distorts overmuch unless temperature kept low. Distorted loads respond well to reconditioning treatment	6
Aspen, Canadian	*Populus tremuloides*	E			Inclined to distort unless special care is taken in piling*	
Avodiré	*Turraeanthus africanus*	E	3·5	2·0	Dries fairly rapidly but with tendency to cup and twist	
Ayan	*Distemonanthus benthamianus*	F			Dries readily with little degrade	
Baikiaea	*Baikiaea insignis*	D	4·5	2·0	Dries fairly rapidly and well but with a tendency to cup appreciably	
Balsa	*Ochroma pyramidale*	H	3·5	2·0	Rather variable in its drying properties. Probable that different schedules desirable for various weight grades but except for heavier weight class, schedule H should prove suitable	2
Banak	*Virola koschnyi*	C	9·0	3·0	Dries rather slowly with a marked tendency to check and split. Distortion may be appreciable, sometimes accompanied by collapse	
Baromalli	*Catostemma commune*	E	9·0	4·5	Dries rather slowly but without extensive degrade	
Basswood	*Tilia americana*	K	5·0	3·5	Dries without undue difficulty*	
Beech, European	*Fagus sylvatica*	D	9·5	4·5	Dries fairly well but must be classed as a moderately refractory species. There is always a tendency for the wood to check, split and distort and shrinkage in drying is large	5

Commercial name	Botanical species	Kiln schedule suggested	Approx. shrinkage %† Tangential	Radial	Kiln drying characteristics	Drying time group
Beech, Southland or silver	*Nothofagus menziesii*	E			Dries fairly easily; some tendency for end splitting but distortion comparatively slight	
Belian	*Eusideroxylon zwageri*	B	4·5	2·0	Surface checks badly even when dried very slowly	
Berlinia	*Berlinia* spp	E	5·0	3·0	Dries rather slowly but well, apart from isolated cases of moderate distortion. There is a pronounced tendency for mould growths to develop and some discoloration may result	
Bintangcr	*Calophyllum* spp	A			Very prone to distort but checking should not be serious*	
Binuang	*Octomeles sumatrana*	C	7·0	3·0	Dries slowly with severe degrade in the form of checking, end splitting and distortion. Knots split rather badly and there is a tendency for fungal stain to develop	
Birch, European	*Betula pubescens* *Betula verrucosa*	F	8·0	5·0	Dries well but with a tendency to distort	3
Birch, yellow	*Betula alleghaniensis*	G	4·5	3·5	Dries rather slowly but with little degrade	
Black bean	*Castanospermum australe*	C	4·0	2·0	Dries slowly with marked tendency to collapse, honeycomb and split. Reconditioning treatment not always effective in removing collapse. Air drying prior to kiln drying is recommended	9

† In drying from green to 12% moisture content
* Information derived from sources other than PRL

Blackbutt	*Eucalyptus pilularis*	C	7·0	4·5	Very prone to check during drying and collapse may occur. Prior air seasoning is advised*
Bombway, white	*Terminalia procera*	E	3·5	2·5	Tends to distort; requires careful stacking
Box, Cape Box, East London	*Buxus macowani*	B			The smaller logs may be dried in the round without splitting but larger ones should be halved or cut into dimensions before drying to obtain satisfactory results. Best results are obtained by air drying the timber very slowly under cover. The main defect encountered is the development of very fine surface checks which often penetrate quite deeply into the wood*
Box, European	*Buxus sempervirens*	B			Dries very slowly with pronounced tendency to develop surface checks. Liable to split if dried in the round but this damage can be minimised if not prevented by soaking the bolts prior to drying in a solution of a chemical such as common salt or urea, provided these chemicals are not objectionable in the subsequent use of the wood
Brush box	*Tristania conferta*	C	7·0	4·0	This species has a very marked tendency to distort. Checking of plain-sawn boards also gives trouble. Some collapse may occur, in which case final reconditioning is recommended*

Commercial name	Botanical species	Kiln schedule suggested	Approx. shrinkage %† Tangential	Radial	Kiln drying characteristics	Drying time group
Cabbage bark, black	*Lonchocarpus castilloi*	G	4·0	2·0	Dries at rather a slow rate but fairly well. Slight tendency to check and for knots to split but the timber distorts very little	
Camphorwood, East African	*Ocotea usambarensis*	G	4·0	2·5	Dries slowly with little degrade but it is particularly difficult to extract moisture from the centre of thick quartered planks	8
Canarium	*Canarium schweinfurthii*	H	4·5	2·5	Dries rather slowly but fairly well. Cross-sectional distortion and collapse may be troublesome and there is a tendency to end split	
Cedar, African pencil	*Juniperus procera*	G	3·0	2·0	Has a marked tendency to fine surface checking and must be considered a slow drying species	
Cedar, South American	*Cedrela fissilis*	H	4·0	3·0	Dries fairly rapidly and satisfactorily though somewhat prone to distort and collapse. Knots tend to split badly but surface checking is not likely to be serious	
Cedar, western red	*Thuja plicata*	J	2·5	1·5	Dries readily in the thinner dimensions but some planks may prove very difficult to dry in the thicker sizes, collapse and honeycombing sometimes occurring in very wet pieces	2
Cedar, yellow	*Chamaecyparis nootkatensis*	J	3·0	1·5		

† In drying from green to 12% moisture content
* Information derived from sources other than PRL

Celtis	*Celtis* spp	H	4·0	2·5	Dries fairly rapidly with little degrade apart from a slight end splitting and distortion	
Cherry, European	*Prunus avium*	A	6·5	3·5	Dries fairly readily but with a pronounced tendency to distort	5
Chestnut, sweet	*Castanea sativa*	D	5·5	3·0	Dries slowly with a marked tendency to collapse, honeycomb and to retain patches of moisture. Only partial recovery effected by reconditioning. Liable to develop golden oak stain	
Chickrassy	*Chukrasia tabularis*	E			Dries quite rapidly with a slight tendency to check and distort and some liability to collapse, though not severely*	
Coachwood	*Ceratopetalum apetalum*	E	11·5	4·5	Dries slowly with a tendency to split and distort. Cupping is considerable owing to the very large shrinkage differential	
Coigüe	*Nothofagus dombeyi*	B			Dries badly with pronounced tendency to distort. Collapse is prevalent in this species which is very variable in its drying properties*	
Cordia	*Cordia* spp	K	2·5	1·5	Dries well with only a slight tendency to bow and twist but liable to retain pockets of moisture	4
Crabwood	*Carapa guianensis*	C	6·0	3·0	Dries fairly well but rather slowly with a tendency to split in the initial stages	
Cramantee	*Guarea excelsa*	E	5·0	2·0	Dries well but rather slowly with a slight tendency to split, check and distort	

Commercial name	Botanical species	Kiln schedule suggested	Approx. shrinkage %† Tangential	Radial	Kiln drying characteristics	Drying time group
Curupay	*Anadenanthera macrocarpa*	G	5·0	2·0	Dries very slowly with little distortion but splitting and checking may be appreciable, especially in the thicker dimensions	
Cypress, southern	*Taxodium distichum*	K			Dries well but very refractory in the thick dimensions*	
Dahoma	*Piptadeniastrum africanum*	A	5·0	2·5	A variable species which dries slowly. Some material exhibits a marked tendency to collapse and distort. Collapse cannot effectively be removed by a reconditioning treatment	7
Danta	*Nesogordonia papaverifera*	E	5·0	3·5	Dries well with comparatively little degrade; some 'ribbing' may occur	8
Dhup	*Canarium euphyllum*	H			Dries easily with practically no degrade from splitting or distortion*	
Dogwood	*Cornus florida*	E			Dries at rather a slow rate but without much splitting or distortion	
Ebony, African	*Diospyros* spp	E	6·5	5·5	Dries in small dimensions fairly quickly and well with little tendency to split or distort	
Ebony, East Indian	*Diospyros* spp	C			The black parts of this timber are reputed to be very difficult to dry as the wood develops long, fine, deep cracks, especially if cut to relatively large dimensions*	

† In drying from green to 12% moisture content
* Information derived from sources other than PRL

Ekki	*Lophira elata*	B	5·5	4·5	An extremely refractory species. Not only does this timber part very slowly with its moisture but severe splitting and some distortion are likely to occur. It needs to be piled with special care	9
Elm, European Elm, Dutch	*Ulmus procera* *Ulmus hollandica*	A	6·5	4·5	Dries fairly well but with a very marked tendency to distort. There is little tendency to check or split apart from a few checks across the grain but there is some tendency to collapse. The timber should be very carefully piled with closely spaced vertical lines of sticks and the top of the load should be weighted down with concrete blocks or other material. Reconditioning applied to the dry wood can be used with advantage to reduce the amount of distortion, shrinkage and collapse	5
Elm, rock	*Ulmus thomasii*	D			Care needed to minimise checking and twist; shrinkage in drying is large*	
Elm, white	*Ulmus americana*	F			The timber dries quite readily and has a medium shrinkage*	
Elm, wych	*Ulmus glabra*	A			Dries fairly well; has a tendency to distort but to a lesser extent than European elm and it is not prone to collapse. The timber should be carefully piled with close spacing of vertical lines of sticks. Shrinkage about the same as in European elm	5

Commercial name	Botanical species	Kiln schedule suggested	Approx. shrinkage %† Tangential	Radial	Kiln drying characteristics	Drying time group
Eng	*Dipterocarpus tuberculatus*	D	7·5		Closely resembles gurjun and has similar drying properties. Slow drying with a tendency to split and check. Air drying prior to kiln drying is recommended*	
Esia	*Combretodendron macrocarpum*	B (10% humidity increase for material over 38 mm thick)	7·0	6·5	Dries slowly and is very prone to check and split in the process. Appreciable distortion is likely to occur. End splitting, checking and shakes may prove serious. Impracticable to kiln dry economically	
'Fir, Douglas'	*Pseudotsuga menziesii*	K	4·0	2·5	Dries rapidly and well without much checking or distortion but knots tend to split and loosen	1
Fir, silver	*Abies alba*	K	5·0	2·0	Dries very rapidly with little tendency to distort but some tendency to check and split and for knots to loosen and split	
Fotie	*Hannoa klaineana*	L			Dries rapidly and well	
Freijo	*Cordia goeldiana*	E			Dries readily and well but with a slight tendency for end splits to develop. Little distortion is likely to occur	
Gaboon	*Aucoumea klaineana*	E			The timber dries readily without excessive distortion or checking. Shrinkage is moderate*	

† In drying from green to 12% moisture content
* Information derived from sources other than PRL

Gedu nohor	*Entandrophragma angolense*	A	5·0	2·5	Dries fairly rapidly with a marked tendency to distort	
Glassy wood	*Guettarda* sp	C	4·0	2·0	Dries rather slowly but fairly well though distortion may be appreciable*	
Greenheart	*Ocotea rodiaei*	B	4·5	3·0	Dries very slowly and with considerable degrade particularly in the thicker sizes. Kiln drying from the green is not an economic proposition for thick greenheart and in practice timber over 25 mm in thickness would have to be partly air dried. Distortion is not serious but checking and splitting tend to be severe	9
Guarea	*Guarea thompsonii* *Guarea cedrata*	E E	4·0 3·5	2·0 2·5	*Guarea thompsonii* dries with little tendency to distort but some tendency to split, requiring care in drying. *Guarea cedrata* dries with very little tendency to split or distort. In both species resin exudation may cause some degrade in the appearance of the dried timber	
Gum, spotted	*Eucalyptus maculata*	C	6·5	5·0	Great care needed if checking of flat-sawn material is to be avoided. On account of the inclined grain common in this species some distortion must be expected. Slight collapse sometimes occurs and reconditioning is not effective*	

† In drying from green to 12% moisture content
* Information derived from sources other than PRL

Commercial name	Botanical species	Kiln schedule suggested	Approx. shrinkage %† Tangential	Radial	Kiln drying characteristics	Drying time group
Gurjun	*Dipterocarpus* spp	D	11·5–7·5	5·5–2·5	Dries slowly even when subjected to high temperatures and considerable difficulty experienced in obtaining uniform drying across the section, especially in quarter-sawn stock. During kiln drying the high temperatures tend to cause exudation of considerable quantities of gummy resin. Slight collapse sometimes occurs and distortion, particularly cupping, is often considerable	7
Haldu	*Adina cordifolia*	E			A slightly refractory timber with some tendency to check and split*	
Hemlock, eastern	*Tsuga canadensis*	K	4·5	2·0	Rather difficult to dry on account of its tendency to twist and careful piling is necessary*	
Hemlock, western	*Tsuga heterophylla*	K	5·0	3·0	When green, the timber has a very high moisture content and does not dry so rapidly or so easily as British Columbian Douglas fir. With care, it can be kiln dried very satisfactorily. The tendency towards fine surface checking needs to be guarded against but distortion is not generally troublesome. Some difficulty may be experienced in extracting moisture from the centres of thick planks	2

Haiariballi	*Alexa leiopetala*	B			Dries extremely badly with excessive collapse. No schedule has been found to yield satisfactory results	
Holly, European	*Ilex aquifolium*	C	12·0	5·0	Dries rather slowly with marked tendency to distort badly	
Hornbeam	*Carpinus betulus*	E	7·0	5·0	Dries well and fairly rapidly	5
Horse-chestnut, European	*Aesculus hippocastanum*	H	3·0	2·0	Dries readily without incurring any significant degrade. No special precautions need be taken to preserve the white colour of the timber	
Idigbo	*Terminalia ivorensis*	J	3·0	1·5	Dries well with little or no checking and only slight splitting of knots. Distortion of all kinds is remarkably small	4
Iroko	*Chlorophora excelsa*	E	2·0	1·5	Dries well without appreciable degrade there being only a slight tendency to split and distort. Stick marks sometimes develop during drying	4
Ironbark	*Eucalyptus* spp	B	8·0	6·0	Very refractory, especially in thick dimensions. Thin quarter-sawn boards can be kiln dried rapidly without checking but in general the timber requires very mild drying conditions. Air drying prior to kiln drying is recommended*	

Commercial name	Botanical species	Kiln schedule suggested	Approx. shrinkage %† Tangential	Radial	Kiln drying characteristics	Drying time group
Jacareuba	*Calophyllum brasiliense*	A	5·5	3·0	Dries slowly with appreciable distortion but little checking. Moisture is extracted from the centres of planks with difficulty	
Jarrah	*Eucalyptus marginata*	C	8·0	5·0	Jarrah is very prone to distort in drying but with careful stacking and weighting much of the inherent distortion can be prevented. Final steaming has not proved successful in reducing distortion. Checking of wide and thick stock may be considerable. Partial air drying prior to kiln drying is recommended*	
Jelutong	*Dyera costulata*	H	3·0	2·0	Easy to dry with little tendency to split or distort although staining is liable to cause trouble. Difficult to extract moisture from the core of thick stock	5
Kapur	*Dryobalanops lanceolata*	H	8·0	3·5	Dries very well apart from cup. Little or no splitting should occur	7
Kapur	*Dryobalanops beccarii*	G	6·5	3·0	Dries fairly well but with tendency to cup and twist. In thick dimensions much more difficult to dry without severe surface checking	

† In drying from green to 12% moisture content
* Information derived from sources other than PRL

Karri	*Eucalyptus diversicolor*	C	10·0	5·0	Has a pronounced tendency to check and in thick pieces the cracks may become very deep. Although much more severe on the tangential face, checking often appears on quarter-sawn material. In spite of the fact that the grain is generally much straighter than that of jarrah, considerable distortion occurs at times in thin stock. Collapse is more prevalent than in jarrah but not as great as in *Eucalyptus regnans*. Periodic steaming is recommended during kiln drying, and air drying prior to kiln drying is advised*	
Kauri, New Zealand	*Agathis australis*	J			Dries well but not rapidly without much checking, distortion or shrinkage. Reported to have appreciable longitudinal shrinkage*	
Kempas	*Koompassia malaccensis*	E			Dries fairly well apart from tendency to check in zones of abnormal tissue*	
Keruing	*Dipterocarpus* spp	D	8·5	4·5	Dries with pronounced tendency for cupping to develop and for existing shakes to extend	7
Kokko	*Albizia lebbeck*	E			A moderately refractory species with some tendency to end splitting and surface checking. A certain amount of longitudinal shrinkage is to be expected*	

Commercial name	Botanical species	Kiln schedule suggested	Approx. shrinkage %† Tangential	Radial	Kiln drying characteristics	Drying time group
Krabak	*Anisoptera* spp	E	6·5	3·0	Dries very slowly with some slight tendency to distort. Drying rate varies considerably and it is difficult to extract moisture from the centres of thick planks	
Kurokai	*Protium decandrum*	C	5·0	3·0	Dries fairly rapidly with marked tendency to cup and twist and for original shakes to extend	
Lapacho	*Tabebuia* spp	E	2·5	1·5	Dries rather slowly but very well	
Larch, European	*Larix decidua*	H	4·0	3·0	Dries fairly rapidly with some tendency to distort and for knots to split and loosen	4
Larch, Japanese	*Larix leptolepis*	H	3·0	2·0	Dries fairly rapidly with tendency to split and check, also to distort but not to same extent as European larch	4
Laurel, Chilean	*Laurelia aromatica*	C			Dries fairly readily but with a definite tendency to collapse. Responds well to a reconditioning treatment	
Laurel, Indian	*Terminalia* spp	C	6·5	4·0	A refractory timber to dry; liable to surface checking, splitting and distortion*	
Lignum vitae	*Guaiacum* spp	B			Very slow and refractory in drying	
Lime, European	*Tilia vulgaris*	H	7·5	5·0	Dries well but with a tendency to distort	
Louro, Red	*Ocotea rubra*	E			Dries at a moderate rate with a tendency to check and split	

† In drying from green to 12% moisture content
* Information derived from sources other than PRL

Maho	*Sterculia pruriens*	A	7·5	3·0	Dries fairly rapidly with tendency to distort	
Mahogany, African	*Khaya* spp	F	4·5	2·5	Dries with little degrade except distortion when strongly developed tension wood is present	4
	Khaya grandifoliola	A	4·5	2·5	Dries fairly well on schedule A without much distortion apart from cup	6
Mahogany, Central American	*Swietenia macrophylla*	F	3·0	2·0	Dries fairly rapidly and well without much checking or distortion	
Makoré	*Tieghemella heckelii*	H	4·5	3·0	Dries with little degrade. Distortion is generally slight but appreciable twist may occur in a small proportion of a load	6
Mansonia	*Mansonia altissima*	H	3·0	1·5	Dries well with very little distortion but knots tend to split appreciably	4
'Maple, Queensland'	*Flindersia brayleyana*	C			In the heavier, close-grained and darker coloured stock of this species cupping and general distortion is considerable and appreciable collapse may occur	
Maple, rock	*Acer saccharum*	E	5·0	2·5	Dries at a slow rate but without undue degrade*	
Matai	*Podocarpus spicatus*	J			Dries fairly quickly without much degrade*	
Mayflower	*Tabebuia pentaphylla*	E			Dries well with little degrade	
Mchenga	*Isoberlinia globiflora*	C	4·5	3·0	Dries slowly with strong tendency for surface checking and distortion to develop	
Mengkulang	*Heritiera simplicifolia*	H	7·0	3·0	Dries well but with a variable tendency to surface check	5

Commercial name	Botanical species	Kiln schedule suggested	Approx. shrinkage %† Tangential	Radial	Kiln drying characteristics	Drying time group
Meranti, dark red light red white	*Shorea* spp	F	6·0	3·0	Most of the many *Shorea* species included in commercial loads of meranti dry without much checking or distortion apart from cup. Thick material tends to surface check and distort, more particularly the dark red meranti (mainly *S. pauciflora*)	5
Meranti, yellow	*Shorea* spp	J	7·0	2·5	Dries rather slowly but well, apart from cup. Tendency to honeycomb in thick sizes	
Missanda	*Erythrophleum guineense*	D			Dries at a slow rate with a tendency to distort*	
Mjombo	*Brachystegia boehmii*	C	5·0	3·5	Dries slowly with appreciable degrade both in distortion, splitting and checking	
Mora	*Mora excelsa*	B	7·5	5·0	Dries very slowly with considerable degrade. Surface checking develops readily and all four forms of distortion are liable to be severe	
Morabukea	*Mora gonggrijpii*	B	7·0	4·0	As for mora	
Mtambara	*Cephalosphaera usambarensis*	J			Dries rapidly with little degrade apart from cup	
Mtondo	*Brachystegia spiciformis*	C	4·0	3·0	Dries slowly with some degrade particularly twist and splitting of knots. Slight ribbing or incipient collapse may develop on quartered boards	

† In drying from green to 12% moisture content
* Information derived from sources other than PRL

Mubura	*Parinari excelsa*	B (10% relative humidity increase for material over 38 mm thick)	5·0	3·0	Dries slowly and is very prone to check and split. Severe distortion may also occur and with thick material air drying before kiln drying is recommended	
Muchenche	*Newtonia buchananii*	J	4·0	2·0	Dries fairly rapidly and with only slight degrade as 25 mm boards. Thicker timber is disproportionately more difficult to dry and some checking, splitting and collapse may develop	
Mugongo	*Ricinodendron rautanenii*	K	2·0	1·5	Dries rapidly with little degrade apart from cup	
Mugwi	*Bosquiea phoberos*	J	4·0	2·5	Dries rapidly and well with very little distortion and only slight tendency to end split	
Muhimbi	*Cynometra alexandri*	B	4·5	2·5	Dries slowly, especially in thick sizes, with a tendency to serious surface checking. Distortion generally is slight	
Muhuhu	*Brachylaena hutchinsii*	B	3·0	2·0	Dries with negligible distortion but in thick material drying is disproportionately more difficult and serious checking tends to develop	8
Mumuli	*Holoptelea grandis*	C			Dries slowly with a tendency to check and distort*	
Muninga	*Pterocarpus angolensis*	J	1·5	1·0	Dries very well though rather slowly especially in thicker sizes of quartered material. Little tendency to split or distort and the knots split only slightly	7

Commercial name	Botanical species	Kiln schedule suggested	Approx. shrinkage %† Tangential	Radial	Kiln drying characteristics	Drying time group
Musizi	*Maesopsis eminii*	F	4·0	2·5	Dries fairly rapidly and very well. Slight distortion but no tendency to split or check and knots remain sound	
Myrtle, Tasmanian	*Nothofagus cunninghamii*	C	6·0	4·0	Very variable in drying properties. Light coloured timber gives little trouble apart from tendency to cup. Darker (red) timber requires very careful drying to avoid serious checking, both surface and internal. Collapse occurs in the red myrtle but this may largely be removed by reconditioning. Preliminary air drying is recommended as is also the segregation of the two classes of timber before kiln drying	
Nargusta	*Terminalia amazonia*	C	5·0	2·5	Dries slowly particularly in thick sizes and with considerable difficulty in removing moisture from the centre of quarter-sawn material. Marked tendency to split and check	
Niangon	*Tarrietia utilis*	E	4·5	2·5	Dries well with distortion only slight apart from twist. Slight end splitting and surface checking may develop	6
Nyatoh	*Palaquium* spp	E			Dries rather slowly with tendency to split and distort*	

† In drying from green to 12% moisture content
* Information derived from sources other than PRL

Oak, American white	*Quercus* spp	C	5·5	3·0	Dries relatively slowly with tendency to check, split and honeycomb	
Oak, American red	*Quercus* spp	C			Dries relatively slowly with tendency to check, split and honeycomb	
Oak, European	*Quercus robur* *Q. petraea*	C	7·5	4·0	Dries with a marked tendency to split and check, particularly in the early stages. Considerable risk of honeycombing if drying is forced. Distortion may be appreciable. Susceptible to yellow stain	9
Oak, Japanese	*Quercus* spp	C			Same tendencies as European oak but not quite so marked	8
'Oak, Silky'	*Cardwellia sublimis*	E	5·0	2·0	Very variable in drying rate but generally little tendency to check, collapse or distort, apart from cup in wide plain-sawn boards	
'Oak, Tasmanian'	*Eucalyptus delegatensis* *E. obliqua* *E. regnans*	C	10·0–6·5	5·0–4·0	Dries with a marked tendency to develop surface checks in the early stages of drying and a slight tendency to distort. The species is very prone to collapse and to check internally. Air drying prior to kilning is recommended and a high temperature reconditioning treatment during the final stage of drying usually proves effective in removing most of the collapse	
Oak, Turkey	*Quercus cerris*	B	11·5	4·0	Dries very slowly with considerable degrade. It is very prone to check and distort (particularly cup) excessively	

Commercial name	Botanical species	Kiln schedule suggested	Approx. shrinkage %† Tangential	Radial	Kiln drying characteristics	Drying time group
Obeche	*Triplochiton scleroxylon*	L	3·0	2·0	Dries very well with practically no tendency to split and only a very slight tendency to distort	1
Odoko	*Scottellia coriacea*	E	5·0	2·5	Dries fairly rapidly with little distortion but a pronounced tendency to split	
Ogea	*Daniellia ogea*	J	4·5	1·5	Dries fairly rapidly with little degrade. Slight distortion and collapse may occur on thick material but these are unlikely to be severe	
Okan	*Cylicodiscus gabunensis*	B	3·5	3·0	Dries slowly with a marked tendency to split and check. Distortion should not be serious	
Okwen	*Brachystegia* spp	E	3·5	2·5	Dries rather slowly with some tendency to check but distortion, particularly cup, the main cause of degrade. Slight collapse may occur	
Olive, East African	*Olea hochstetteri*	E	6·5	4·0	Dries slowly with a tendency to check and split. Honeycombing may develop in thick material; also pronounced cross-sectional distortion	7
Omu	*Entandrophragma candollei*	A	6·0	4·0	Dries without checking but with a marked tendency to distort	7

† In drying from green to 12% moisture content
* Information derived from sources other than PRL

Opepe	*Nauclea diderrichii*	E	4·0	2·0	Quarter-sawn material dries with very little checking or distortion but flat-sawn timber is difficult to dry without appreciable checking and splitting occurring	7
Padauk, African	*Pterocarpus soyauxii*	J	2·0	1·0	Dries very well with a minimum of degrade	4
Padauk, Andaman	*Pterocarpus dalbergioides*	F			Dries well without much checking or distortion*	
Padauk, Burma	*Pterocarpus macrocarpus*	F			Rather slow drying but with a comparatively low percentage of degrade from splitting and distortion*	
Panga panga	*Millettia stuhlmannii*	E			Dries very slowly with little degrade*	
Pear	*Pyrus communis*	A	9·0	4·5	Dries slowly with a definite tendency to distort	
Peroba rosa	*Aspidosperma* spp	E			Dries without much splitting but some distortion may develop	
Peroba, white	*Paratecoma peroba*	D	3·5	2·0	Dries readily and well with negligible splitting. Distortion not generally serious though fairly severe twisting occasionally occurs	
Persimmon	*Diospyros virginiana*	C	6·5	4·5	Dries fairly rapidly with some tendency to check	
Pillarwood	*Cassipourea malosana*	A	6·0	2·5	Dries rather slowly with considerable degrade, especially in thicker dimensions. Cup and twist are frequently severe. Slight collapse is probable and checking appreciable. Kiln drying from green cannot be recommended for material over 38 mm thick	

Commercial name	Botanical species	Kiln schedule suggested	Approx. shrinkage %† Tangential	Radial	Kiln drying characteristics	Drying time group
Pine, Caribbean pitch Pine, British Honduras pitch	*Pinus caribaea* *Pinus oocarpa*	H	6·0	3·0	Dries rather slowly with some tendency to split and check in the early stages and a marked tendency to distort	
'Pine, Chile'	*Araucaria araucana*	J	5·0	2·5	Dries fairly rapidly but inclined to retain patches of moisture. Numerous small knots tend to split but no checking likely and distortion, in general, slight	
Pine, Corsican	*Pinus nigra* var *maritima*	M	5·0	2·5	Dries well without much degrade apart from split knots and some resin exudation. Owing to the liability of the sapwood of the green timber to develop blue-stain no time should be lost between conversion and loading into the kiln for drying	1
Pine, Jack	*Pinus banksiana*	L			Dries without difficulty and with little degrade*	
Pine, locgepole	*Pinus contorta* var *latifolia*	L	4·0	2·5	Dries very rapidly and well with no checking or splitting. Distortion mainly slight but moderate bow and twist occasionally. Resin exudation fairly general	

† In drying from green to 12% moisture content
* Information derived from sources other than PRL

'Pine, Parana'	*Araucaria angustifolia*	D			More difficult to dry than most softwoods and rather variable in its drying properties. The darker coloured material being very prone to split, distort and dry rather slowly, the load should be weighted to minimise distortion and a conditioning period is often necessary to ensure uniformity of final moisture content. Inherent stresses and abnormal wood are liable to cause longitudinal distortion on machining into small sizes	2
Pine, Ponderosa	*Pinus ponderosa*	L			Dries readily but susceptible to stain*	
Pine, radiata	*Pinus radiata*	K	4·0	2·5	Dries rapidly with little degrade but timber from immature trees warps appreciably owing to spiral grain and knots*	
Pine, red	*Pinus resinosa*	L			Dries easily and uniformly with little checking or distortion*	
Pine, Scots	*Pinus sylvestris*	M	4·5	3·0	Dries well though knots tend to split and dead knots to loosen. Owing to its tendency to blue-stain the wood should be loaded into the kiln with as little delay as possible. If light colour to be retained, schedule F* should be employed	1 3*

† In drying from green to 12% moisture content
* Information derived from sources other than PRL

Commercial name	Botanical species	Kiln schedule suggested	Approx. shrinkage %† Tangential	Radial	Kiln drying characteristics	Drying time group
Pine, yellow (Pine, Weymouth)	*Pinus strobus*	L	3·5	1·5	Dries easily and uniformly though care has to be exercised to prevent staining, especially of the sapwood. When brown stain is not objectionable, schedule L can be used. To avoid brown stain developing both temperatures and relative humidities should be kept lower and the greatest possible ventilation given during the early stages of drying	1
Plane, London	*Platanus hybrida*	E	9·0	4·0	Dries fairly rapidly without much splitting but with some distortion	
Podo	*Podocarpus* spp	A	4·0	2·5	Dries fairly rapidly but has a tendency to split, check and distort. It is recommended that the timber pile should be heavily weighted to restrain distortion; subject to compression wood which shrinks longitudinally	
Poplar, black Italian	*Populus canadensis* var *serotina*	E	5·5	2·0	Dries fairly well but local pockets of moisture are apt to remain in the timber	6
Pterygota	*Pterygota kamerunensis*	H	5·0	2·0	Dries fairly rapidly with slight tendency to surface check. Distortion small though cup may sometimes be appreciable. There is a tendency for 'sticker stain' to develop	

Punah	*Tetramerista glabra*	C			Dries readily with tendency to cup, end split and stain*	
Purpleheart	*Peltogyne* spp	E	4·5	2·0	Dries well with little degrade but in thicker stock difficulty in extracting moisture from the centre	6
Pyinkado	*Xylia xylocarpa*	C			Some tendency to surface check, split and distort*	
Quaruba	*Vochysia* spp	A	6·0	2·0	Dries fairly rapidly with little tendency to check but marked inclination to distort particularly in the form of twist and cup. Some collapse may occur in thicker stock; reconditioning only partly effective	
Ramin	*Gonystylus bancanus*	C + 10% rh for material over 38 mm thick	5·0	2·5	Dries readily with little distortion but with tendency for end splitting and surface checking to develop. Such degrade liable to be severe when drying timber thicker than 38 mm	4
Rauli beech	*Nothofagus procera*	E	4·5	2·5	Dries rather slowly but with little degrade	
Robinia	*Robinia pseudoacacia*	A			Dries slowly with a marked tendency to distort	
Rosewood, Honduras	*Dalbergia stevensonii*	C			Dries at a slow rate with a marked tendency to check*	
Rosewood, Indian	*Dalbergia latifolia*	E			Dries well, the colour improving during the process*	6
Sapele	*Entandrophragma cylindricum*	A	4·5	2·5	Dries fairly well though with a marked tendency to distort	5
Satinwood, Ceylon	*Chloroxylon swietenia*	C			Dries fairly well but with a tendency to surface check*	
Sepetir	*Pseudosindora palustris*	G	3·0	2·0	Dries very well, distortion in all forms being small	7

Commercial name	Botanical species	Kiln schedule suggested	Approx. shrinkage %† Tangential	Radial	Kiln drying characteristics	Drying time group
Seraya—see Meranti						
Serrette	*Byrsonima spicata*	E	6·0	3·0	Dries rather slowly but quite well in 25 mm material, cup being the worst defect. Degrade increases more than usual with increase of thickness	
Spruce, eastern Canadian	*Picea glauca*	K	4·0	2·0	Dries fairly easily*	
Spruce, Engelmann	*Picea engelmannii*	K			Dries without difficulty with no serious degrade*	
Spruce, European	*Picea abies*	K	4·0	2·0	Dries well with little tendency to split, check or distort though some splitting and loosening of knots must be expected. Susceptible to stain	1
Spruce, Sitka	*Picea sitchensis*	J	5·0	3·0	Dries well though some splitting and loosening of knots occurs and in timber sawn from small trees twist may be severe especially in quarter-sawn pieces	1
Sterculia, brown	*Sterculia rhinopetala*	B	9·5	5·0	Dries with severe cupping, though other forms of distortion slight. Appreciable checking and end splitting may occur and slight collapse is likely	9
Sterculia, yellow	*Sterculia oblonga*	C	6·5	3·5	Dries with marked tendency to surface check, end split and cup. Slight collapse may occur	8

† In drying from green to 12% moisture content
* Information derived from sources other than PRL

Sycamore	*Acer pseudoplatanus*	A if light colour important otherwise E‡	6·5	3·5	Dries well but temperatures should be kept below 50°C if darkening of the timber is to be avoided. To eliminate the sticker stain liable to occur in sycamore, it is sometimes first air dried by end racking (see page 27)	6 5‡
Tallowwood	*Eucalyptus microcorys*	C			A very refractory species which is prone to check severely. Air drying prior to kilning recommended*	
Tawa	*Beilschmiedia tawa*	E	5·0	3·0	Dries fairly readily but with some tendency to check	
Teak	*Tectona grandis*	H	2·5	1·5	Dries well but extra care required in determining moisture contents, as differences in drying rate are occasionally large. The timber is liable to become varied in colour during drying but the variation disappears within a reasonably short time after exposure of the surfaces	4
'Teak, Rhodesian'	*Baikiaea plurijuga*	D	2·5	1·5	Dries well with little degrade	8
Thitka	*Pentacme burmanica*	E			Dries at a slow rate without much degrade*	
Totara	*Podocarpus totara*	J			Dries quickly and well*	
Tupelo	*Nyssa aquatica*	E			Dries fairly readily without undue splitting. Some of the material may distort very severely and it is advisable to weight the load*	

Commercial name	Botanical species	Kiln schedule suggested	Approx. shrinkage %† Tangential	Radial	Kiln drying characteristics	Drying time group
Turpentine	*Syncarpia glomulifera*	C	6·0	4·0	Tends to check and distort in drying. Collapse occurs but can usually be removed by a reconditioning treatment. Partial air drying prior to kiln drying recommended*	
Utile	*Entandrophragma utile*	A	3·5	3·0	Dries readily without splitting or checking though existing shakes may extend considerably. Distortion occurs, mainly in the form of twist, which may be severe in low-quality timber	5
Virola, light	*Virola surinamensis*	C			Often sustains a great deal of degrade in drying*	
Wallaba	*Eperua falcata*	B +10% rh for material over 38 mm thick	8·5	4·0	Dries very slowly with marked tendency to check, split, distort and honeycomb	
'Walnut, African'	*Lovoa trichiliodes*	E	5·0	2·0	Dries without much degrade	5
Walnut, American black	*Juglans nigra*	E	4·5	3·0	Dries rather slowly with a liability to honeycomb	
Walnut, European	*Juglans regia*	E	5·5	3·0	Dries well but tends to honeycomb in the thicker dimensions	5
'Walnut, Queensland'	*Endiandra palmerstonii*	E	6·5	4·0	Dries fairly readily in thinner sizes but some tendency to distort. Slight collapse may occur which can be removed by reconditioning. Thick material liable to check unless quarter sawn	

† In drying from green to 12% moisture content
* Information derived from sources other than PRL

Wamara	*Swartzia leiocalycina*	B	5·0	3·0	Dries slowly with appreciable surface checking and end splitting but distortion not serious	
Wattle, black	*Acacia mollissima*	A	7·0	4·0	Dries readily with pronounced distortion particularly cupping	
White star apple	*Chrysophyllum albidum*	E	4·5	2·5	Dries rather slowly with little distortion but pronounced tendency to end split	
Willow	*Salix* spp	H (for cricket bats D)			Dries well but local pockets of moisture are apt to remain in the timber and special care is required in testing for moisture content to ensure that reasonable uniformity is achieved	3
Yellowwood, British Honduras	*Podocarpus guatemalensis*	H	3·5	2·0	Dries at a moderate rate with some tendency to split and check but little inclination to distort	
Yew	*Taxus baccata*	G	3·5	2·0	Dries fairly rapidly and well but with a tendency for shakes to open	4

Other species

Little or no definite information is available on the shrinkage values and detailed drying characteristics of a number of other species which may have to be kiln dried. It is possible, however, from limited data and from a knowledge of their general properties, to suggest drying schedules which should be suitable for many of these timbers, and these are listed below.

It must be emphasised that these schedules are given chiefly as a guide to the operator drying any species for the first time and he may well be able to modify them to advantage as experience is gained.

Timber Commercial name	Botanical name	Schedule
African silky-oak	(see grevillea p. 129)	
akomu	(see ilomba p. 129)	
alder, red	*Alnus rubra*	J
amarillo	*Centrolobium ochroxylon*	E
American whitewood	*Liriodendron tulipifera*	E
andiroba	(see crabwood p 103)	
aningeria	*Aningeria altissima*	C
apitong	*Dipterocarpus* spp	D
aspen, European	*Populus tremula*	E
assacu	(see hura p. 129)	
baboen	(see virola p. 126)	
bagac	(see apitong p. 128)	
banga wanga	*Amblygonocarpus andongensis*	B
birch, paper	*Betula papyrifera*	H
black gum	(see tupelo p. 125)	
blackwood, African	*Dalbergia melanoxylon*	B
blackwood, Australian	*Acacia melanoxylon*	E
'boxwood, Knysna'	*Gonioma kamassi*	C
'Burma cedar'	*Cedrela toona*	H
butternut	*Juglans cinerea*	E
cativo	*Prioria copaifera*	C
'cedar, Burma'	*Cedrela toona*	H
'cedar, Port Orford'	*Chamaecyparis lawsoniana*	J
'cedar, white'	*Thuja occidentalis*	J
ceiba	*Ceiba pentandra*	J
chan	*Shorea* spp	D
chuglam, white	*Terminalia bialata*	E
chumprak	*Tarrietia cochinchinensis*	C
cocuswood	*Brya ebenus*	A
cornel	(see dogwood p. 104)	
cottonwood	*Populus* spp	H
courbaril	*Hymenaea courbaril*	C
dalli	(see virola p. 126)	
daniellia	(see ogea p. 118)	
degame	*Calycophyllum candidissimum*	B
determa	(see louro, red p. 112)	
Elgon olive	(see loliondo p. 129)	
espavel	*Anacardium excelsum*	E
fernan sanchez	*Triplaris guayaquilensis*	E
fir, alpine	*Abies lasiocarpa*	L
fir, amabilis	*Abies amabilis*	L
fir, balsam	*Abies balsamea*	L

Timber Commercial name	Botanical name	Schedule
fir, grand	*Abies grandis*	L
fir, noble	*Abies procera*	L
geronggang	*Cratoxylon arborescens*	E
grevillea	*Grevillea robusta*	C
guayacan	*Tabebuia* sp	E
gum, black	(see tupelo p. 125)	
gum, southern blue	*Eucalyptus globulus*	C
gum, saligna	*Eucalyptus saligna*	C
hackberry	*Celtis occidentalis*	H
hickory	*Carya glabra*	E
'hoop pine'	*Araucaria cunninghamii*	J
'huon pine'	*Dacrydium franklinii*	K
hura	*Hura crepitans*	E
ilomba	*Pycnanthus angolensis*	C
imbuya	*Phoebe porosa*	E
Indian silver-grey wood	*Terminalia bialata*	E
jequitiba	*Cariniana* sp	D
jigua	*Ocotea* spp	H
kamassi	(see 'Knysna boxwood')	
kanluang	(see haldu p. 108)	
kanyin	(see gurjun p. 108)	
katon	*Sandoricum indicum*	E
'Knysna boxwood'	*Gonioma kamassi*	C
kokrodua	(see afrormosia p. 98)	
landa	*Erythroxylum manii*	E
larch, Siberian	*Larix russica*	H
larch, tamarack	*Larix laricina*	K
larch, western	*Larix occidentalis*	K
lauan	*Shorea* spp, *Parashorea* spp and *Pentacme* spp	E
laurel, Ecuador	(see salmwood p. 130)	
locust	(see courbaril p. 128)	
loliondo	*Olea welwitschii*	E
longui rouge	*Chrysophyllum* sp	E
maccarati	*Burkea africana*	B
mafu	*Fagaropsis angolensis*	C
magnolia	*Magnolia* spp	E
manio	*Podocarpus nubigenus*	J
maple, Norway	*Acer platanoides*	E
maple, soft	*Acer saccharinum* or *rubrum*	E
melawis	(see ramin p. 123)	
merbau	*Intsia bijuga*	C
mersawa	*Anisoptera* spp	E
mkuka	*Ficalhoa laurifolia*	F
muave	(see missanda p. 114)	
mueri	*Pygeum africanum*	C
mugonyone	*Apodytes dimidiata*	C
mujwa	(see alstonia p. 98)	
musine	*Croton megalocarpus*	C
'New Zealand white pine'	*Podocarpus dacrydioides*	J
nongo	*Albizia grandibracteata*	F
ntola	(see agba p. 98)	
nyankom	(see niangon p. 116)	

Timber Commercial name	Botanical name	Schedule
oak, Persian	*Quercus castaneaefolia*	B
okoko	(see sterculia, yellow p. 124)	
okoumé	(see gaboon p. 106)	
okuro	(see albizia, West African p. 98)	
olive, Elgon	(see loliondo p. 129)	
olivier, white	(see nargusta p. 116)	
olivillo	*Aextoxicon punctatum*	E
partridgewood	*Caesalpinia granadillo*	C
pecan	*Carya* spp	E
pine, American pitch	*Pinus palustris*	L
pine, Austrian	*Pinus nigra*	M
pine, Canadian red	*Pinus resinosa*	L
'pine, huon'	*Dacrydium franklinii*	K
pine, longleaf pitch	(see pine, American pitch)	
pine, maritime	*Pinus pinaster*	M
'pine, New Zealand white'	*Podocarpus dacrydioides*	J
pine, shortleaf pitch	*Pinus echinata*	L
pine, sugar	*Pinus lambertiana*	L
pine, western white	*Pinus monticola*	L
poplar, Canadian	*Populus balsamifera*	E
poplar, grey	*Populus canescens*	E
poplar, white	*Populus alba*	E
'Port Orford cedar'	*Chamaecyparis lawsoniana*	J
pradoo	(see padauk, Burma p. 119)	
pycnanthus	(see ilomba p. 129)	
redwood, European	(see pine, Scots p. 121)	
redwood, Californian	(see sequoia p. 130)	
rimu	*Dacrydium cupressinum*	K
saligna gum	*Eucalyptus saligna*	C
salmwood	*Cordia alliodora*	E
sandbox	(see hura p. 129)	
Santa Maria	*Calophyllum brasiliense* var *rekoi*	A
satinwood, African	*Fagara macrophylla*	C
satinwood, East Indian	(see satinwood, Ceylon p. 123)	
sempilor	*Dacrydium elatum*	K
semul	*Bombax insigne*	K
sequoia	*Sequoia sempervirens*	K
seraya, red	*Shorea* spp	F
seraya, white	*Parashorea malaanonan*	J
seraya, yellow	*Shorea faguetiana*	J
silky-oak, African	(see grevillea p. 129)	
silver-grey wood, Indian	*Terminalia bialata*	E
sipo	(see utile p. 126)	
'southern cypress'	*Taxodium distichum*	K
'S. American cedar'	*Cedrela fissilis*	H
spruce, black	*Picea mariana*	K
spruce, red	*Picea rubens*	K
tali	(see missanda p. 114)	
tamarack larch	*Larix laricina*	K
taukkyan	(see Laurel Indian p. 112)	
thingan	*Hopea odorata*	C
tola branca tola, white	(see agba p. 98)	
toon	(see 'Burma cedar' p. 128)	
ulmo	*Eucryphia cordifolia*	C

Timber Commercial name	Botanical name	Schedule
vinhatico	*Plathymenia reticulata*	E
waika chewstick	*Symphonia globulifera*	C
wawa	(see obeche p. 118)	
'white cedar'	*Thuja occidentalis*	J
white chuglam	*Terminalia bialata*	E
white olivier	(see nargusta p. 116)	
whitewood (in part)	*Picea abies* (see spruce p. 124)	K
whitewood, American	*Liriodendron tulipifera*	E
yang	*Dipterocarpus* spp	E
yemeri	(see quaruba p. 123)	
yon	*Anogeissus acuminata*	C
zebrano	*Microberlinia brazzavillensis*	B

Appendix B Standard kiln drying schedules

For possible modifications to these standard schedules see section 9.4 of this manual.

Schedule A

	Temperature °C		Relative humidity	Temperature °F	
	Dry-bulb	**Wet-bulb**	**% (approx.)**	**Dry-bulb**	**Wet-bulb**
Green	35	30·5	70	95	87
60	35	28·5	60	95	83
40	40	31	50	104	88
30	45	32·5	40	113	91
20	50	35	35	122	95
15	60	40·5	30	140	105

Schedule B

	Temperature °C		Relative humidity	Temperature °F	
	Dry-bulb	**Wet-bulb**	**% (approx.)**	**Dry-bulb**	**Wet-bulb**
Green	40	37·5	85	104	100
40	40	36·5	80	104	98
30	45	40·5	75	113	105
25	50	44	70	122	111
20	55	46	60	131	115
15	60	47·5	50	140	118

Schedule C

	Temperature °C		Relative humidity	Temperature °F	
	Dry-bulb	**Wet-bulb**	**% (approx.)**	**Dry-bulb**	**Wet-bulb**
Green	40	37·5	85	104	100
60	40	36·5	80	104	98
40	45	40·5	75	113	105
35	45	39·5	70	113	103
30	45	38·5	65	113	101
25	50	42	60	122	107
20	60	47·5	50	140	118
15	65	48·5	40	149	119

Schedule D

	Temperature °C Dry-bulb	Wet-bulb	Relative humidity % (approx.)	Temperature °F Dry-bulb	Wet-bulb
Green	40	37·5	85	104	100
60	40	36·5	80	104	98
40	40	35	70	104	95
35	45	37·5	60	113	99
30	45	35	50	113	95
25	50	36·5	40	122	98
20	60	40·5	30	140	105
15	65	44	30	149	111

Schedule E

	Temperature °C Dry-bulb	Wet-bulb	Relative humidity % (approx.)	Temperature °F Dry-bulb	Wet-bulb
Green	50	47	85	122	117
60	50	46	80	122	115
40	50	45	75	122	113
30	55	47·5	65	131	118
25	60	49	55	140	121
20	70	54·5	45	158	130
15	75	57·5	40	167	136

Schedule F

	Temperature °C Dry-bulb	Wet-bulb	Relative humidity % (approx.)	Temperature °F Dry-bulb	Wet-bulb
Green	50	45	75	122	113
60	50	44	70	122	111
40	50	42	60	122	107
30	55	43·5	50	131	110
25	60	46	45	140	115
20	70	52·5	40	158	127
15	75	57·5	40	167	136

Schedule G

	Temperature °C Dry-bulb	Wet-bulb	Relative humidity % (approx.)	Temperature °F Dry-bulb	Wet-bulb
Green	50	47	85	122	117
60	50	46	80	122	115
40	55	51	80	131	124
30	60	54·5	75	140	130
25	70	62·5	70	158	145
20	75	62·5	55	167	145
15	80	61	40	176	141

Schedule H

	Temperature °C Dry-bulb	Wet-bulb	Relative humidity % (approx.)	Temperature °F Dry-bulb	Wet-bulb
Green	60	55·5	80	140	132
50	60	54·5	75	140	130
40	60	52	65	140	126
30	65	53·5	55	149	129
20	75	57·5	40	167	136

Schedule J

	Temperature °C Dry-bulb	Wet-bulb	Relative humidity % (approx.)	Temperature °F Dry-bulb	Wet-bulb
Green	60	53	70	140	128
50	60	50·5	60	140	123
40	60	47·5	50	140	118
30	65	48·5	40	149	119
20	75	52	30	167	126

Schedule K

	Temperature °C Dry-bulb	Wet-bulb	Relative humidity % (approx.)	Temperature °F Dry-bulb	Wet-bulb
Green	70	65	80	158	149
50	75	67	70	167	153
30	80	68·5	60	176	155
20	90	69	40	194	156

Schedule L

	Temperature °C Dry-bulb	Wet-bulb	Relative humidity % (approx.)	Temperature °F Dry-bulb	Wet-bulb
Green	80	72	70	176	161
40	90	69	40	194	156

Schedule M

	Temperature °C Dry-bulb	Wet-bulb	Relative humidity % (approx.)	Temperature °F Dry-bulb	Wet-bulb
Green	90	81	70	194	178
50	95	78	50	203	172

Appendix C
Kiln drying times

To the question frequently asked—how long does timber take to dry in a kiln?—the overall average answer for UK operations is about 10 days. This figure, however, conceals a very wide range of times for individual kiln runs which can be anything from 1 to 50 days or more. It is largely useless for such purposes as appraising the performance of a particular kiln installation and its operation, production scheduling of drying plant, determining required kiln capacities in new plant, and estimating the likely cost of drying. No basis exists on which an accurate time for any particular kiln run can be determined in advance, but by taking account of the more important of the many factors involved, a useful estimate is possible. For the timber, these factors include species, thickness, moisture content reduction and initial quality. The particular kiln plant used also affects drying rate, as does the approach of plant personnel to the drying process, and the final timber quality and moisture uniformity for which they aim. This appendix provides a basis for making approximate estimates of drying times.

The method adopted falls into two broad stages. First, a basic drying time is established which takes account only of species, thickness and moisture content reduction. The data on which this is based were obtained from PRL species evaluation tests, using equipment that can be regarded as average for UK commercial installations. For this purpose, species are classified into 9 groups and the drying rates of these range from very fast (group 1) to very slow (group 9). These drying rates obtain when using the recommended PRL schedules. Second, the effects of timber quality (and indirectly of operational approach to drying) and kiln plant are taken into account. These aspects are applied in adjusting the basic drying time to provide an estimate for the particular kiln plant and circumstances.

Basic drying time

The basic drying time for a load of timber is obtained by multiplying together three distinct factors. The first of these is the Drying Time Factor (C) for the relevant Species Group (G) and is given in Table C1. The group into which each species of known drying characteristics is placed, together with the recommended kiln schedule, is indicated in Appendix A.

The second factor, given in Table C2 (p. 139), depends on the Moisture Content Reduction (R) to be effected in the kiln and the third, the Thickness Factor (T) is determined by the Timber Thickness (P) (Table C3, p. 139).

Example: Red seraya 44 mm thick is to be dried from 45 to 15 per cent moisture content. It is seen from Appendix A that red seraya is in species group 5 (recommended PRL schedule K) and from Table C1 that the drying time factor for this group is 1·0. The moisture content reduction is to be 30 per cent and Table C2 shows that this requires 12·1 drying time units (days). Finally Table C3 shows the thickness factor for 44 mm material to be 1·2. The basic drying time estimate is therefore:
$1{\cdot}0 \times 12{\cdot}1 \times 1{\cdot}2 = 14{\cdot}5$ days.

Table C3 gives factors only for the thicknesses commonly dried in kilns—viz from 25 mm to 70 mm. Many timbers become progressively more difficult, and usually uneconomical to kiln dry, in thicknesses of over 70 mm. The increase in drying time will generally be much more than simply proportional to the increase in thickness.

Thin boards on the other hand become relatively easier to dry, this being particularly true of refractory species. Lower humidities can be applied without causing surface checking and drying times should be reduced at least in proportion to the reduction in thickness below 25 mm. For any given thickness, very narrow boards will dry faster than those of normal width. The estimated basic drying times for square cross-sections may be taken as about half of those for planks of the same thickness.

Variations from basic time in practice

The time actually taken to dry can vary considerably from the basic time as estimated from Tables C1–C3. A composite factor has to be applied to cover the effects of the drying plant equipment, the operational approach and the initial and final quality of the timber dried.

Effect of equipment

The basic drying times were compiled from the results obtained when applying standard FPRL schedules in medium air-speed kilns with adequate heating and ventilation. Drying rates will tend to be faster in high air-speed kilns, and lower in the older low air-speed units in which the heating and ventilation are also sometimes inadequate. The effect of air speed is more marked on green timber and/or fast drying species.

For the purpose of arriving at the composite correction factors given in Table C4 kiln plants are broadly classified as follows:

Plant class	Characteristics of kiln plant
1	high air-speed, over 1·5 metres/sec (5 feet/sec) ample heating surfaces and ventilation (mainly applies to side fan kilns)
2	medium air-speed, 0·9 to 1·2 metres/sec (3 to 4 feet/sec) adequate heating and ventilation (mainly cross-shaft overhead fan kilns)
3	low air-speed, below 0·9 metres/sec (3 feet/sec) ventilation often inadequate heating and steam supply sometimes inadequate (mainly longitudinal fan shaft kilns)

Effect of the type of control

Automatic control equipment for steam valves, ventilators and fan reversal make it practicable to maintain the desired schedule at all times. It is usually possible therefore to achieve somewhat faster drying than in manually controlled kilns, in which, for instance, overnight and weekend settings have to be made on the safe side. Allowance for this effect is made by selecting column A (Automatic) or M (Manual) in Table C4 when determining the Composite Plant Drying Factor (K).

Effect of initial and final timber quality and operational approach

The initial quality of the timber to be dried to some extent influences the kiln treatment applied and hence the drying time. Hardwood timbers with large knots and irregular or spiral grain call for lower temperatures than clear straight grained material. Timber which has surface checked in preliminary drying has to be given higher than normal humidities to avoid excessive extension of the checks.

Another factor which can considerably influence the drying time is the amount of final degrade acceptable and this will obviously depend greatly on the exact purpose for which the timber is to be used. (This is not always known, as in the case of timber dried by merchants for stock.) Strongly linked with this aspect of kiln drying is the manner in which an operator approaches the task. If overanxious about the possibility of spoiling valuable timber an unnecessarily mild schedule may be applied, resulting in increased drying time and hence increased cost.

At the other extreme, having had experience with a particular material, and knowing that a certain amount of degrade is acceptable for its end use, an operator may quite rightly achieve faster drying by applying conditions more severe than those given in the standard PRL schedule.

The overall effect of these various aspects, which are difficult to quantify, is covered by selecting levels of 'initial timber quality' and 'final degrade permissible' from the following.

Initial timber quality	**Final degrade permissible**
High	Above normal
Average	Normal
Low	Minimal

A candid appraisal of the drying operation is necessary. Thus a cautious approach must be rated as one aiming at minimal final degrade; low quality output relative to the average for the industry is above normal. Initial timber quality must be rated in relation to the best available in the species to be dried.

The terms used in this rating, which are necessarily rather vague, are incorporated in Table C4. It will be noted that obtaining the minimum degrade with low quality timber leads, as would be expected, to increased drying times, and above normal degrade with high quality timber leads to a reduction.

Estimating plant drying time

Having made an estimate of basic drying time, this is modified by application of the plant drying factor (K) to arrive at the estimate for the particular kiln plant and timber being dried. It will be seen that a wide variation from basic time is possible; this reflects the wide variation that is actually recorded within the industry.

Example: Consider again the 44 mm seraya examined earlier. Suppose the kiln to be an overhead cross-shaft design with medium air speed and manual control of conditions. Further, that the timber is of average quality and that degrade has to be minimised. By reference to Table C4 and following the steps indicated it is seen that for this combination of circumstances the plant drying factor is 1·25 and therefore the estimated drying time becomes $1{\cdot}25 \times 14{\cdot}5 = 18{\cdot}1$, say 18 days. If, on the other hand, the seraya is to be dried in a fast air speed kiln with automatic control and a normal amount of degrade is allowable, the factor would then be 0·80 and the estimated drying time $0{\cdot}80 \times 14{\cdot}5 = 11{\cdot}6$ (say 12) days.

Further examples of use of the drying times tables

1 100 × 50 mm hemlock to be dried from green to 12 per cent in a high air-speed automatically controlled kiln. The timber is of average quality and above normal degrade can be tolerated. Hemlock is in species group 1 (from Appendix A).

Basic drying time = C × D × T = 0·3 × 23·3 × 1·4 = 9·8 days
Plant factor K = 0·55
Estimated drying time = 0·55 × 9·8 = 5·4 (say 6) days

2 50 × 50 mm squares of beech to be dried from 25 per cent to 10 per cent in a low air-speed manually controlled kiln. The beech is of average quality and degrade must be minimal. Beech is in species group 5.

Basic drying time = 1·0 × 7·6 × 1·4 = 10·6 days

Reduction of 50 per cent because squares and not planks brings basic time down to 5·3 days.

Plant factor K = 1·4
Estimated drying time = 1·4 × 5·3 = 7·4 (say 8) days

It must be emphasised again that such estimates can only be approximate. Successive loads even of the same species and thickness in the same kiln can show appreciable differences in drying times.

The situation in the drying industry is not entirely static of course. Although major improvements in drying plant and techniques seem unlikely there is nevertheless a trend in this direction which is tending to reduce kilning times.

Table C1

Species group	Drying time factor
G	C
1	0·3
2	0·4
3	0·55
4	0·75
5	1·0
6	1·3
7	1·6
8	1·95
9	2·35

Table C2

Moisture content reduction—per cent	Drying time units—days
R	D
15	7·6
20	9·2
25	10·7
30	12·1
35	13·4
40	14·6
45	15·8
50	17·0
55	18·1
60	19·2
65	20·3
70	21·3
75	22·3
80	23·3

Table C3

Timber thickness mm	Thickness factor
P	T
25	0·6
32	0·8
38	1·0
44	1·2
50	1·4
57	1·65
63	1·9
70	2·15

Table C4
Plant drying factors (K)

Operational approach		Kiln plant class					
		Class 1 High airspeed (mainly side-fan)		Class 2 Medium airspeed (mainly cross-shaft)		Class 3 Low airspeed (mainly longitudinal shaft)	
		Control					
Final degrade permissible	Initial quality of timber	A (automatic)	M (manual)	A (automatic)	M (manual)	A (automatic)	M (manual)
Above normal	High	0·50	0·55	0·60	0·65	0·80	0·85
	Average	0·55	0·60	0·75	0·80	0·90	0·95
	Low	0·60	0·65	0·80	0·85	1·00	1·05
Normal	High	0·70	0·75	0·90	0·95	1·05	1·10
	Average	0·80	0·85	1·00	1·05	1·15	1·20
	Low	0·90	0·95	1·10	1·15	1·25	1·30
Minimal	High	0·90	0·95	1·10	1·15	1·25	1·30
	Average	1·00	1·05	1·20	1·25	1·35	1·40
	Low	1·10	1·15	1·30	1·35	1·45	1·50

Appendix D
The re-drying of timber after impregnation with water-borne preservatives

The impregnation treatment of timber with a water-borne preservative leaves the moisture content of the material at a high level, even higher than in its natural green state, especially in the permeable sapwood zones. Although rendered much more durable by the process, the wood is not fit for use in many circumstances until it has been re-dried. The shrinkage and any accompanying distortion may well be excessive if wet treated wood is used.

Treated timber can be kiln dried in the normal way and usually it will tolerate the schedule suggested for untreated wood of the same species. However, relative humidities some 5 or 10 per cent higher may be needed for timber which has surface checked in drying prior to impregnation. The outer layers may have been compressed during treatment due to the reverse moisture gradient set up and the closed checks may open up and extend if the surfaces are re-dried too fast.

It has been found that water treated timber, especially in the high moisture content zones, dries appreciably slower than untreated wood of the same size and species. For instance, when drying treated 50 mm Scots pine to an average of 18 per cent for window joinery, cross cutting has revealed small, wet pockets and the moisture content of these has proved to be as high as 50 to 60 per cent. The kiln runs have to be prolonged considerably to dry out such pockets.

The slower drying of the treated wood is thought to be due mainly to the lowering of the permeability of the wood during the initial drying to below 30 per cent moisture content prior to impregnation.

To improve uniformity and reduce the times taken in the kilns it is advisable, whenever possible, to air dry the very wet treated timber for several weeks before finishing off the drying in a kiln.

Timber treated with fire retardant chemicals such as ammonium phosphate/ammonium sulphate also dries slower than untreated timber under similar conditions. Owing to the increased hygroscopicity of the treated wood, however, it has been found that humidities lower than usual can be employed and the time reduced to the same as that for untreated timber.

On the other hand if the treated timber is to be used in load-bearing components the temperatures should be kept at a low level since re-drying at high temperatures has been found to diminish its strength appreciably.

The effect of various preservative treatments on the electrical properties of timber and hence on the readings obtained with moisture meters has been discussed under section 1.4.3.

Although the corrosive action of the vapour coming from treated timber during re-drying is slight, it is advisable that in kilns used regularly for drying such material, particular attention should be paid to keeping the shell, fans, pipes, etc, well painted.

Appendix E
Kilning defects

Causes and possible prevention or remedies

Defect	Causes	Prevention or reduction to minimum	Possible remedies
Casehardening	Too rapid surface drying owing to use of too low humidity in early stages and/or too high temperature in later stages	Use higher humidities in early stages and limit temperature in final stages	At the end of the kiln run: Long conditioning period, or a relief treatment, viz, raise temperature 20°F and humidity to 90 per cent for 2 to 6 hours according to severity of stresses
Surface checking	Too rapid drying of surface in relation to the core	Use higher humidities in early stages Test accuracy of wet- and dry-bulb readings	No cure obviously—checks will tend to close when wood fully dried to uniform moisture content
End splitting	Ends drying more rapidly than the rest owing to:		
	End grain drying	Paint ends with, eg, bituminous paint	None
	Overhanging ends	Pile properly with sticks at or very near ends of rows	
	Too much circulation over ends and too little through stack	Baffle off ends and make all air go through stack	
	Restraint imposed by end cleats putting shrinking ends in tension	Remove cleats before kiln drying	

Defect	Causes	Prevention or reduction to minimum	Possible remedies
Honeycombing	Severe casehardening in early stages followed by internal checking from excessive stressing in centre Too high temperature in final stages	Use higher humidities in early stages Periodic steaming Limit final temperatures	None
Collapse	Surface tension exerted on cell walls as free water leaves them. Pronounced in a few species and in timber which is waterlogged. Occurrence increased by use of too high a temperature	Use low temperature schedule	Apply reconditioning treatment, viz 4 to 8 hours steaming at 100°C and saturation—preferably when moisture content in region of 15 per cent
Distortion			
Cup	Differential shrinkage across grain in tangential and radial directions	Cannot be prevented but all forms of distortion can be minimised by the following: Pile very carefully, viz place sticks at frequent intervals and in perfect alignment; place sticks at ends of all boards; avoid overhanging ends, eg by box-piling	Apply reconditioning treatment as for collapse but if piling bad dismantle stack and re-pile properly before steaming
Spring and Bow	Differential shrinkage along the grain owing to irregular or curved grain or reaction wood		
Twist	Spiral grain or interlocked or irregular grain		
All forms of distortion	Improper piling of timber, eg uneven sticks; sticks at too great intervals or placed out of vertical alignment; unsupported ends of boards High temperatures causing greater shrinkage and hence increased distortion Overdrying	Use lower temperature schedule Place heavy weights on top of stack Leave out low grade material with very irregular grain	Condition to the correct moisture content

Uneven drying	Too much variation from one part of kiln to another in:		Long final conditioning treatment
	Temperature	Improve arrangement or drainage of heating coils	
	Humidity	Make sure that steam spray is uniform along length	
	Air circulation	Check fan speed	
		Improve air distribution, eg by fitting deflecting baffles	
		Stop all possible short circuiting of stack	
	Leaks in steam pipes	Repair leaks	
	Leaking doors	Improve door fitting	
	Drips from ceiling	Use ceiling coils	
Mould growth	Poor circulation	Speed up circulation	Steam for 3 hours at 160°F
	Very slow drying at moderate temperatures	Use higher temperature if species not one liable to distort or collapse badly.	

Appendix F

Table F1. The relation between wet-bulb hygrometer readings and equilibrium moisture contents of wood at various air temperatures in a kiln.

Dry-bulb (°C)	Wet-bulb (°C)									
35·0	21·7	23·2	24·5	25·7	27·0	28·0	28·8	29·7	30·4	31·1
37·5	23·7	25·3	26·7	28·0	29·2	30·3	31·2	32·1	32·8	33·6
40·0	25·7	27·4	28·9	30·3	31·5	32·7	33·6	34·6	35·3	36·0
42·5	27·7	29·5	31·1	32·5	33·9	35·1	36·1	37·0	37·8	38·5
45·0	29·8	31·7	33·3	34·8	36·3	37·5	38·5	39·4	40·3	41·0
47·5	31·9	33·9	35·6	37·1	38·7	39·9	41·0	42·0	42·7	43·5
50·0	34·0	36·3	38·1	39·5	41·1	42·4	43·5	44·4	45·3	46·1
52·5	36·0	38·4	40·4	41·9	43·5	44·9	46·0	47·0	47·8	48·6
55·0	38·5	40·6	42·8	44·3	45·9	47·0	48·5	49·4	50·3	51·1
57·5	40·8	43·1	45·3	46·9	48·5	49·8	51·0	52·1	52·8	53·7
60·0	43·0	45·5	47·7	49·4	51·0	52·4	53·6	54·6	55·3	56·2
62·5	45·3	48·0	50·3	51·9	53·5	55·0	56·2	57·2	57·9	58·7
65·0	47·7	50·5	52·8	54·6	56·1	57·6	58·8	59·7	60·4	61·3
67·5	50·2	53·1	55·3	57·2	58·6	60·1	61·3	62·4	63·1	63·9
70·0	52·8	55·7	57·9	59·6	61·3	62·6	64·0	64·9	65·7	66·4
72·5	55·3	58·2	60·5	62·3	64·0	65·3	66·7	67·6	68·3	69·1
75·0	57·8	60·6	63·1	64·8	66·5	68·0	69·3	70·1	71·0	71·7
77·5	60·4	63·3	65·7	67·5	69·2	70·7	71·9	72·7	73·6	74·3
80·0	63·0	66·0	68·5	70·1	71·8	73·3	74·5	75·4	76·3	77·0
82·5	65·7	68·7	71·0	72·8	74·5	75·9	77·1	78·1	78·9	79·7
85·0	68·4	71·3	73·7	75·4	77·2	78·6	79·8	80·7	81·5	82·3
87·5	71·2	74·1	76·5	78·1	79·9	81·3	82·5	83·4	84·2	85·0
90·0	74·0	76·9	79·2	80·8	82·6	84·0	85·1	86·1	86·8	87·6
Moisture content %	6	7	8	9	10	11	12	13	14	15

Dry-bulb (°F)	Wet-bulb (°F)									
95	70	73	75	78	80	82	84	85	86	88
100	74	77	79	82	84	86	88	90	91	92
105	78	81	83	86	89	91	93	95	96	98
110	82	86	89	91	94	96	98	100	101	103
115	86	90	93	96	99	101	103	105	106	108
120	90	94	98	101	104	106	108	110	111	113
125	94	99	103	106	109	111	113	115	116	118
130	100	104	108	111	114	116	118	120	122	123
135	105	109	113	116	118	121	123	125	127	128
140	110	114	118	121	123	126	128	130	132	133
145	115	119	123	126	129	131	133	135	137	138
150	120	124	128	131	134	136	139	140	142	143
155	125	129	133	136	139	141	144	145	146	148
160	130	134	138	141	144	147	149	151	152	153
165	135	139	143	146	150	153	155	156	157	158
170	140	144	148	152	155	158	160	161	163	164
175	146	149	153	157	160	163	165	166	167	169
180	152	155	159	162	165	168	170	172	173	175
185	157	160	165	168	171	174	176	177	178	179
190	162	166	170	173	176	179	181	183	184	185
195	167	171	175	180	182	184	186	188	189	191
Moisture content %	6	7	8	9	10	11	12	13	14	15

The above values are approximate only, but are applicable to most of the common commercial timbers.

Table F2. (°C)
Table of relative humidity (or per cent of saturation)

Dry-bulb (°C) — Difference between readings of wet- and dry-bulbs in degrees Centigrade

Dry-bulb (°C)	0·5	1·0	1·5	2	2·5	3	3·5	4	4·5	5	5·5	6	6·5	7	7·5	8	8·5	9	9·5	10	10·5	11	11·5	12	12·5	13	13·5	14	14·5	15	15·5	16	16·5	17	17·5	18	18·5	19	19·5	20	20·5	21
30	96	92	88	85	81	78	75	71	68	65	62	58	55	52	49	46	44	41	39																							
31	96	93	88	85	81	78	76	72	68	65	62	59	56	53	50	47	45	42	40																							
32	96	93	89	86	82	79	76	72	69	66	63	60	57	54	51	48	46	43	41																							
33	97	93	89	86	82	79	76	73	70	67	64	61	58	55	52	49	47	44	42	39																						
34	97	93	90	86	83	80	77	73	70	67	64	62	59	56	53	50	48	45	43	40	38																					
35	97	93	90	86	83	80	77	74	71	68	65	62	60	57	54	51	48	46	45	41	39																					
36	97	93	90	87	83	80	77	74	71	68	65	63	60	57	55	52	49	47	45	42	40	37																				
37	97	94	90	87	84	81	78	75	72	69	66	63	61	58	55	53	50	48	46	43	41	38																				
38	97	94	91	87	84	81	78	75	72	69	66	64	61	59	56	54	51	49	46	44	42	39																				
39	97	94	91	88	84	81	79	75	72	70	67	65	62	59	57	54	52	50	47	45	43	40	38																			
40	97	94	91	88	85	82	79	76	73	70	67	65	62	60	57	55	53	51	48	46	44	41	39	37																		
41	97	94	91	88	85	82	79	76	73	71	68	66	63	61	58	56	53	51	49	47	44	42	40	38																		
42	97	94	91	88	85	82	79	76	74	71	68	66	63	61	59	56	54	52	50	47	45	43	41	39																		
43	97	94	91	88	85	83	80	77	74	72	69	66	64	62	59	57	55	53	50	48	46	44	42	40	38																	
44	97	94	91	88	85	83	80	77	75	72	69	67	64	62	60	58	56	53	51	49	47	45	43	41	39																	
45	97	94	91	88	85	83	80	77	75	72	70	67	65	63	61	58	56	54	52	50	48	46	44	42	40	38																
46	97	94	91	89	86	83	80	78	75	73	70	68	65	63	61	59	56	54	52	50	48	46	44	42	41	39																
47	97	94	92	89	86	83	81	78	75	73	71	68	66	64	62	59	57	55	53	51	49	47	45	43	41	40	38															
48	97	94	92	89	86	84	81	78	76	74	71	69	66	64	62	60	58	56	54	52	50	48	46	44	42	40	38															
49	97	94	92	89	86	84	81	79	76	74	71	69	67	65	63	60	58	56	54	52	50	48	47	45	43	41	39															
50	97	94	92	89	86	84	81	79	76	74	72	69	67	65	63	61	59	57	55	53	51	49	47	45	44	42	40	38														
51	97	95	92	89	87	84	82	79	77	74	72	70	67	65	64	61	59	57	55	53	51	50	48	46	44	42	41	39														
52	97	95	92	89	87	84	82	79	77	75	72	70	68	66	64	62	60	58	56	54	52	50	48	47	45	43	41	40	38													
53	97	95	92	89	87	85	82	80	77	75	73	70	68	66	64	62	60	58	56	54	52	51	49	47	46	44	42	41	39													
54	97	95	92	90	87	85	82	80	77	75	73	71	68	67	65	63	60	59	57	55	53	51	49	48	46	44	43	41	39													
55	97	95	92	90	87	85	82	80	78	76	73	71	69	67	65	63	61	59	57	55	53	52	50	48	47	45	43	42	40	39												
56	97	95	93	90	87	85	83	80	78	76	74	72	69	67	65	64	62	60	58	56	54	52	50	49	47	46	44	42	41	40												
57	97	95	93	90	87	85	83	80	78	76	74	72	70	68	66	64	62	60	58	56	55	53	51	49	48	46	44	43	41	40												
58	97	95	93	90	88	85	83	81	78	76	74	72	70	68	66	64	62	60	59	57	55	53	51	50	48	47	45	43	42	41	39											
59	97	95	93	90	88	85	83	81	79	77	74	72	70	68	66	65	63	61	59	57	55	54	52	50	49	47	45	44	42	41	40											
60	97	95	93	90	88	86	83	81	79	77	75	73	71	69	67	65	63	61	59	57	55	54	52	51	49	48	46	44	43	42	40	39										
61	97	95	93	90	88	86	83	81	79	77	75	73	71	69	67	65	63	61	60	58	56	55	53	51	50	48	46	45	43	42	41	39										
62	97	95	93	90	88	86	84	81	79	77	75	73	71	69	67	65	64	62	60	58	56	55	53	52	50	49	47	45	44	43	41	40										
63	98	95	93	90	88	86	84	82	80	77	75	73	72	69	68	66	64	62	60	59	57	55	54	52	51	49	47	46	44	43	42	40										
64	98	95	93	91	88	86	84	82	80	78	76	74	72	70	68	66	64	63	61	59	57	56	54	53	51	50	48	46	45	44	42	41	39									
65	98	95	93	91	88	86	84	82	80	78	76	74	72	70	68	66	65	63	61	59	58	56	55	53	52	50	48	47	45	44	43	41	40									

	0·5	1·0	1·5	2	2·5	3	3·5	4	4·5	5	5·5	6	6·5	7	7·5	8	8·5	9	9·5	10	10·5	11	11·5	12	12·5	13	13·5	14	14·5	15	15·5	16	16·5	17	17·5	18	18·5	19	19·5	20	20·5	21
66	98	95	93	91	89	86	84	82	80	78	76	74	72	70	68	67	65	63	61	60	58	56	55	53	52	50	49	47	46	45	43	42	41	39								
67	98	95	93	91	89	86	84	82	80	78	76	74	72	70	69	67	65	64	62	60	58	57	56	54	53	51	49	48	46	45	44	42	41	40	38							
68	98	95	93	91	89	87	84	82	80	78	76	75	73	71	69	67	66	64	62	60	59	57	56	54	53	51	50	48	47	46	44	43	42	40	39							
69	98	95	93	91	89	87	84	83	81	79	77	75	73	71	69	68	66	64	62	61	59	58	56	55	53	52	50	49	47	46	45	43	42	41	39							
70	98	95	93	91	89	87	85	83	81	79	77	75	73	71	69	68	66	64	63	61	59	58	56	55	53	52	50	49	48	46	45	44	42	41	40	39						
71	98	95	93	91	89	87	85	83	81	79	77	75	73	71	70	68	66	65	63	61	60	58	57	55	54	52	51	49	48	47	45	44	43	42	40	39						
72	98	96	93	91	89	87	85	83	81	79	77	75	73	72	70	68	67	65	63	62	60	59	57	56	54	53	51	50	49	47	46	45	43	42	41	39						
73	98	96	93	91	89	87	85	83	81	79	77	76	74	72	70	69	67	65	63	62	60	59	57	56	54	53	52	50	49	47	46	45	44	42	41	40						
74	98	96	93	91	89	87	85	83	81	79	78	76	74	72	70	69	67	65	64	62	61	59	58	56	55	53	52	51	49	48	46	45	44	43	42	40						
75	98	96	94	91	90	87	85	83	82	80	78	76	74	72	71	69	67	66	64	62	61	59	58	56	55	54	52	51	50	48	47	46	44	43	42	41						
76	98	96	94	92	90	87	85	84	82	80	78	76	74	73	71	69	68	66	64	63	61	60	58	57	55	54	53	51	50	49	47	46	45	44	42	41						
77	98	96	94	92	90	88	86	84	82	80	78	76	75	73	71	70	68	66	64	63	61	60	59	57	56	54	53	52	50	49	48	46	45	44	43	42	40	39				
78	98	96	94	92	90	88	86	84	82	80	78	77	75	73	71	70	68	66	65	63	62	60	59	57	56	55	53	52	51	49	48	47	45	44	43	42	41	40				
79	98	96	94	92	90	88	86	84	82	80	78	77	75	73	72	70	68	67	65	64	62	60	59	58	56	55	54	52	51	50	48	47	46	45	44	42	41	40				
80	98	96	94	92	90	88	86	84	82	80	79	77	75	73	72	70	69	67	65	64	62	61	59	58	56	55	54	53	51	50	49	47	46	45	44	43	42	40	39	38		
81	98	96	94	92	90	88	86	84	82	81	79	77	75	74	72	70	69	67	66	64	63	61	60	58	57	55	54	53	52	50	49	48	47	45	44	43	42	41	40	39		
82	98	96	94	92	90	88	86	84	83	81	79	77	75	74	72	71	69	67	66	64	63	61	60	59	57	55	54	53	52	50	50	48	47	46	45	43	42	41	40	39		
83	98	96	94	92	90	88	86	84	83	81	79	77	76	74	72	71	69	68	66	65	63	62	60	59	58	56	55	53	52	51	50	49	47	46	45	44	43	42	40	39		
84	98	96	94	92	90	88	86	85	83	81	79	77	76	74	72	71	70	68	66	65	63	62	61	59	58	56	55	54	52	51	50	49	48	46	45	44	43	42	41	40		
85	98	96	94	92	90	88	86	85	83	81	79	78	76	74	73	71	70	68	67	65	64	62	61	59	58	57	55	54	53	52	50	49	48	47	46	44	43	42	41	40		
86	98	96	94	92	90	88	87	85	83	81	80	78	76	75	73	71	70	68	67	65	64	62	61	60	58	57	56	54	53	52	51	50	48	47	46	45	44	42	41	40	39	38
87	98	96	94	92	90	88	87	85	83	82	80	78	76	75	73	72	70	69	67	65	64	63	61	60	59	57	56	55	53	52	51	50	48	47	46	45	44	43	42	41	40	39
88	98	96	94	92	90	89	87	85	83	82	80	78	77	75	74	72	70	69	67	66	64	63	61	60	59	57	56	55	54	52	51	50	49	48	47	45	44	43	42	41	40	39
89	98	96	94	92	90	89	87	85	83	82	80	78	77	75	74	72	71	69	67	66	65	63	62	60	59	58	56	55	54	53	51	50	49	48	47	46	45	43	42	42	40	39
90	98	96	94	92	91	89	87	85	83	82	80	78	77	75	74	72	71	69	68	66	65	63	62	61	59	58	57	55	54	53	52	51	49	48	47	46	45	44	43	42	41	40

Table F3
Table of relative humidity (or per cent of saturation)

Dry-bulb (°F)	Difference between readings of wet- and dry-bulbs in degrees Fahrenheit 1	2	3	4	5	6	7	8	9	10	11	12	13	14	15	16	17	18	19	20	22	24	26	28	30	32	34	36	38	40	45	50	55	60	70	Dry-bulb (°F)
30	89	78	67	56	46	36	26	16	6	0	0																									30
35	91	81	72	63	54	45	36	27	19	10	2	0																								35
40	92	83	75	68	60	52	45	37	29	22	15	7	0	0																						40
45	93	86	78	71	64	57	51	44	38	31	25	18	12	6	0	0																				45
50	93	87	80	74	67	61	55	49	43	38	32	27	21	16	10	5	0	0																		50
55	94	88	82	76	70	65	59	54	49	43	38	33	28	23	19	14	9	5	0	0																55
60	94	89	83	78	73	68	63	58	53	48	43	39	34	30	26	21	17	13	9	5	0															60
65	95	90	85	80	75	70	66	61	56	52	48	44	39	35	31	27	24	20	16	12	5	0														65
70	95	90	86	81	77	72	68	64	59	55	51	48	44	40	36	33	29	25	22	19	12	6	0	0												70
75	96	91	86	82	78	74	70	66	62	58	54	51	47	44	40	37	34	30	27	24	18	12	7	1	0											75
80	96	91	87	83	79	75	72	68	64	61	57	54	50	47	44	41	38	35	32	29	23	18	12	7	3	0										80
85	96	92	88	84	80	76	73	70	66	63	59	56	53	50	47	44	41	38	35	32	27	22	17	13	8	4	0	0								85
90	96	92	89	85	81	78	74	71	68	65	61	58	55	52	49	47	44	41	39	36	31	26	22	17	13	9	5	1	0							90
95	96	93	89	85	82	79	75	72	69	66	63	60	57	54	52	49	46	43	42	38	34	30	25	21	17	13	9	6	2	0						95
100	96	93	89	86	83	80	77	73	70	68	65	62	59	56	54	51	49	46	44	41	37	33	28	24	21	17	13	10	7	4						100
102	96	93	89	86	83	80	77	74	71	69	65	62	59	57	54	52	49	47	45	43	38	34	30	26												102
104	96	93	90	86	83	80	77	74	71	69	65	63	60	58	55	52	50	48	46	43	39	35	31	27	23											104
106	96	93	90	87	83	80	77	74	72	69	66	63	60	58	55	53	51	48	46	44	40	36	32	28	24	21										106
108	96	93	90	87	84	81	78	75	72	70	66	64	61	59	56	54	51	49	47	45	41	37	33	29	26	22	19									108
110	96	93	90	87	84	81	78	75	72	70	67	64	62	60	57	55	52	50	48	46	41	37	34	30	27	23	20	17								110
112	96	93	90	87	84	81	78	75	73	70	67	65	62	60	57	55	53	51	49	47	42	38	35	31	28	24	21	18	15							112
114	97	93	90	87	84	81	78	75	73	71	68	65	63	61	58	56	53	51	49	47	43	39	35	32	28	25	22	19	16	13						114
116	97	93	90	88	84	82	79	76	74	71	68	66	63	61	59	56	54	52	50	48	44	40	36	33	29	26	24	20	17	14						116
118	97	93	91	88	85	82	79	76	74	71	68	66	64	62	59	57	54	53	51	49	44	41	37	34	30	27	24	21	19	15						118
120	97	94	91	88	85	82	79	77	74	72	69	66	64	62	60	57	55	53	51	49	45	41	38	34	31	28	25	22	19	16	10					120
122	97	94	91	88	85	82	79	77	75	72	69	67	65	63	60	58	56	54	52	50	46	42	38	35	32	29	26	23	20	17	12					122
124	97	94	91	88	85	83	80	77	75	72	70	67	65	63	61	58	56	54	52	51	46	43	39	36	33	29	27	24	21	18	13					124
126	97	94	91	88	86	83	80	78	75	73	70	68	65	64	61	59	57	55	53	51	47	43	40	37	33	30	28	25	22	19	14					126
128	97	94	91	89	86	83	80	78	76	73	71	68	66	64	61	59	57	55	53	52	47	44	40	37	34	31	28	25	23	20	15					128
130	97	94	91	89	86	83	80	78	76	73	71	68	66	64	62	60	58	55	54	52	48	44	41	38	35	32	29	26	24	21	15	10				130

132	97	94	92	89	86	83	81	78	76	74	71	69	67	65	62	60	58	56	54	53	49	45	42	39	35	32	30	27	24	22	16	11				132
134	97	94	92	89	86	84	81	79	76	74	71	69	67	65	63	61	59	57	55	53	49	46	42	39	33	31	31	28	25	23	17	12				134
136	97	94	92	89	86	84	81	79	77	74	72	69	67	65	63	61	59	57	55	53	50	46	43	40	37	34	31	28	26	24	18	13				136
138	97	94	92	89	86	84	81	79	77	74	72	70	68	66	63	62	60	58	56	54	50	47	43	40	37	35	32	29	27	24	19	14				138
140	97	94	92	89	87	84	81	79	77	75	72	70	68	66	64	62	60	58	56	54	51	47	44	41	38	35	33	30	27	25	19	14	10			140
142	97	94	92	89	87	84	82	80	77	75	73	70	68	66	64	62	60	58	57	55	51	48	44	42	39	36	33	30	28	26	20	15	11			142
144	97	95	92	89	87	84	82	80	78	75	73	71	69	67	65	63	61	59	57	55	52	48	45	42	39	36	34	31	29	26	21	16	11			144
146	97	95	92	90	87	85	82	80	78	75	73	71	69	67	65	63	61	59	57	56	52	49	45	43	40	37	35	32	29	27	21	17	12			146
148	97	95	92	90	87	85	82	80	78	76	73	71	69	67	65	63	61	60	58	56	53	49	46	43	40	38	35	32	30	28	22	17	13			148
150	98	95	92	90	87	85	82	80	78	76	74	72	70	68	66	64	62	60	58	57	53	49	46	43	41	38	36	33	30	28	23	18	13			150
152	98	95	93	90	88	85	83	81	79	76	74	72	70	68	66	64	62	60	59	57	53	50	47	44	41	39	36	33	31	29	23	19	14	10		152
154	98	95	93	90	88	85	83	81	79	77	74	72	70	68	66	65	62	61	59	57	54	50	47	44	42	39	37	34	32	29	24	19	15	11		154
156	98	95	93	90	88	85	83	81	79	77	74	72	71	69	66	65	63	61	59	57	54	51	48	45	42	40	37	34	32	30	24	20	15	11		156
158	98	95	93	90	88	86	83	81	79	77	75	73	71	69	67	65	63	61	60	58	55	51	48	45	43	40	38	35	33	30	25	20	16	12		158
160	98	95	93	90	88	86	83	81	79	77	75	73	71	69	67	65	64	62	60	58	55	52	49	46	43	41	38	35	33	31	25	21	17	13		160
162	98	95	93	90	88	86	84	82	80	77	75	73	71	69	68	66	64	62	60	59	55	52	49	46	44	41	39	36	34	31	26	22	17	13		162
164	98	95	93	91	88	86	84	82	80	78	75	73	72	70	68	66	64	62	61	59	56	52	49	47	44	41	39	36	34	32	26	22	18	14		164
166	98	95	93	91	88	86	84	82	80	78	76	74	72	70	68	66	65	63	61	59	56	53	50	47	44	42	39	37	35	32	27	23	18	14		166
168	98	95	93	91	88	86	84	82	80	78	76	74	72	70	68	67	65	63	61	60	56	53	50	47	45	42	40	37	35	33	28	23	19	15		168
170	98	95	93	91	89	86	84	82	80	78	76	74	72	70	69	67	65	63	62	60	57	53	50	48	45	43	40	38	35	33	28	24	19	15		170
172	98	95	93	91	89	86	84	82	81	78	76	74	73	71	69	67	66	64	62	60	57	54	51	48	46	43	41	38	36	34	28	24	20	16		172
174	98	95	93	91	89	87	84	83	81	78	76	75	73	71	69	67	66	64	62	61	57	54	51	49	46	43	41	39	36	34	29	24	20	16		174
176	98	96	93	91	89	87	85	83	81	79	77	75	73	71	70	68	66	64	63	61	58	55	52	49	46	44	42	39	37	35	29	25	21	17	10	176
178	98	96	93	91	89	87	85	83	81	79	77	75	73	72	70	68	66	64	63	61	58	55	52	49	47	44	42	39	37	35	30	25	21	17	11	178
180	98	96	93	91	89	87	85	83	81	79	77	75	73	72	70	68	67	65	63	62	58	55	52	50	47	45	42	40	38	35	30	26	22	18	11	180
182	98	96	93	91	89	87	85	83	81	79	77	75	74	72	70	68	67	65	63	62	59	56	53	50	48	45	43	40	38	36	31	26	22	18	12	182
184	98	96	93	92	89	87	85	83	82	79	77	76	74	72	70	69	67	65	64	62	59	56	53	50	48	45	43	41	38	36	31	27	22	19	12	184
186	98	96	94	92	90	87	85	83	82	80	78	76	74	72	71	69	67	66	64	62	59	56	53	51	48	46	43	41	39	37	32	27	23	19	13	186
188	98	96	94	92	90	87	85	84	82	80	78	76	74	73	71	69	68	66	64	63	59	57	54	51	49	46	44	41	39	37	32	27	23	20	13	188
190	98	96	94	92	90	88	85	84	82	80	78	76	75	73	71	69	68	66	65	63	60	57	54	51	49	46	44	42	39	37	32	28	24	20	14	190
200	98	96	94	92	90	88	86	84	82	80	79	77	75	74	72	70	69	67	66	64	61	58	55	53	51	48	46	43	41	39	34	30	26	22	16	200
205	98	96	94	92	90	88	86	84	83	81	79	77	76	74	72	71	69	68	66	65	62	59	56	54	51	49	46	44	42	40	35	31	27	23	17	205
210	98	96	94	93	90	88	87	85	83	81	80	78	76	75	73	71	70	68	67	65	62	60	57	54	52	49	47	45	43	41	36	32	28	24	18	210

Temperature scales

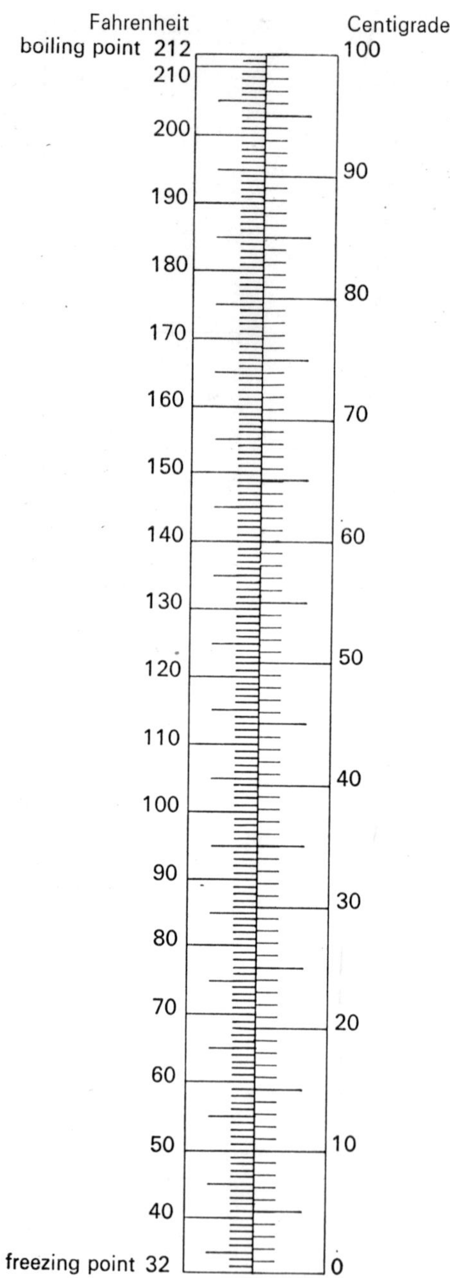

Printed in England for Her Majesty's Stationery Office By McCorquodale Printers Ltd., London
Dd 504540 K20 9/74